K101 An introduction to health and social care

The Open U

Block 6

The shaping of care services in the UK

This publication forms part of an Open University course K101 *An introduction to health and social care*. Details of this and other Open University courses can be obtained from the Student Registration and Enquiry Service, The Open University, PO Box 197, Milton Keynes MK7 6BJ, United Kingdom, tel. +44 (0)845 300 60 90, email general-enquiries@open.ac.uk.

Alternatively, you may visit the Open University website at www.open.ac.uk where you can learn more about the wide range of courses and packs offered at all levels by The Open University.

To purchase a selection of Open University course materials visit www.ouw.co.uk or contact Open University Worldwide, Walton Hall, Milton Keynes MK7 6AA, United Kingdom for a brochure; tel. +44 (0)1908 858793; fax +44 (0)1908 858787; email ouw-customer-services@open.ac.uk.

The Open University
Walton Hall, Milton Keynes
MK7 6AA

First published 2009.

Edited and designed by The Open University.

Typeset in India by Alden Prepress Services, Chennai.

Printed and bound in Malta by Gutenberg Press Limited.

ISBN 978 0 7492 4647 1

1.1

Contents

Introduction to Block 6

In the first five blocks of K101 you have been introduced to a variety of people who give and receive health and social care services. You have been finding out about how and where services are provided and how they are experienced by those who use them. The ways in which these services are shaped are to a great extent determined by the policies that underpin them and this is the subject of the first two units in this block.

Unit 21 takes you back to the founding of the welfare state in the mid-1940s. You will examine the principles that underpinned it and consider the extent to which those principles have survived in the intervening years. Unit 22 focuses on some of the key developments that have taken place in UK society over the last few decades regarding, for example, family composition, employment patterns, the age and ethnic make-up of the population, and inequality. You will consider how health and social care services are changing in response to these developments. In particular, you will look at ways in which the needs of an increasingly diverse society are being approached.

As you work through these two units, you will be asked to think back to people and places you have already come across in the course. This will help you not only to draw together some of the threads running through the earlier blocks you have studied, but also to begin the process of revision prior to the end-of-course exam. Unit 23, the final unit of the course, is devoted entirely to revision and gives you the opportunity to plan how you will go about this.

Overall, these three units should help you to consolidate your learning on K101 and we hope you will find them rewarding reading.

Unit 21

How health and social care developed in the UK

Prepared for the course team by Ken Blakemore and Julia Johnson

Contents

Introduction

This unit examines how health and social care services have come to have the 'shape' or form they do in the UK in the early twenty-first century. Two or three decades ago, many of the important issues and changes that you have learned about in earlier parts of the course – for instance, Direct Payments, care packages and the idea of a 'care market' – were unheard of. Knowing where things have come from helps us to understand where we are now, and why. So we will be starting this unit with the story of how the welfare state was set up. Then we will look at how it developed and was transformed into what it had become at the end of the twentieth century.

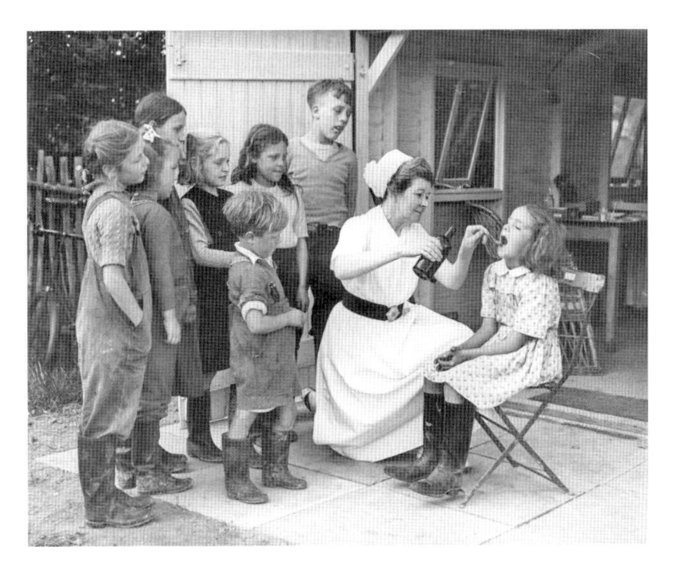

Children in the 1950s reaping the benefit of the new free NHS

Mrs Thatcher (centre right) hands over a copy of the house deeds to James Patterson, the Greater London Council's 12,000th council house buyer, August 1980

As you work through this unit you will find that a lot of significant milestones are mentioned, which chart the history of health and social care. These include the legislation and key events that set up and subsequently shaped the welfare state. To summarise all this information and make it easier to remember, you will find it helpful to create your own 'timeline' as you work through the unit. This will help you to develop your own mental picture of 'what happened when' and to place your own life within that picture.

DVD

Activity 1 Keeping a timeline

Allow about 20 minutes

To simplify this activity, there is a blank timeline on the DVD, along with instructions for getting started. Find Block 6, Unit 21, Activity 1 on the DVD.

Comment

With your printed timeline alongside you, you can now read Unit 21, filling in health and social care milestones as you go. You can also note down any thoughts that come to you about ways in which you and your family were affected by changes in policy and practice.

Learning skills: Reading and note making

In K101 you have explored a variety of ways of making notes, including bullet point notes, mind maps and grids. This timeline is a special kind of note-making grid – structured to reflect the passage of time. The structuring simplifies note making, because you don't have to think about how to organise the notes. The main challenge is working out how much to write down.

That depends on why you are making the notes and what uses you expect to make of them. As you know, notes serve a range of functions. They help you to keep your *attention focused* as you read. They help you to *think* about what you are reading. They help you to *structure* what your mind is taking in (and structure, of course, is fundamental to memory). They can help you to *connect* what you read with events in your own life (again boosting memory). And they also serve *practical functions*, such as helping you to prepare an essay or, in the present context, to prepare for an exam.

In effect, filling in the timeline as you read will help you to convert the ideas and information represented in the words out there on the page into ideas and information embedded in the structures of your mind – thereby assisting in making the ideas and information part of what you know and think. Also, by the end, your completed grid will be a very useful revision aid. It will provide you with a brief overview of the unit. So when it comes to deciding how much to write down, you have to weigh up whether you are writing enough to achieve sufficient engagement with the unit text, or whether you are writing too much and slowing yourself down, interfering with your flow of thoughts and creating a document too detailed to provide a handy overview. This is something you will have to review as you go along.

A key theme of the learning skills strand of K101 is that note making is central to learning. In the process of writing things down (a) you engage actively with what you are studying, and (b) you translate that into terms that are meaningful to you. In this way you help yourself to assimilate knowledge rather than letting it float by you.

Core questions

- What are the underlying principles and ideas on which the UK welfare state is based?
- What major changes in direction have occurred in government's approach to the welfare state since it was introduced?
- What did the twentieth-century welfare state achieve for health and social care?

Are you taking the IVR?

If you are studying K101 as part of the Integrated Vocational Route (IVR), don't forget to check your VQ Candidate Handbook to see which Unit 21 activities contribute to your electronic portfolio.

1 The vision: an all-inclusive welfare state

How and why did a welfare state develop in the UK? What kind of world was it born into? By beginning with the early life of the welfare state we will be able to see how health and social care fit into the story.

What is a welfare state?

A welfare state can be defined as a country, such as the UK, in which the government takes lead responsibility for the welfare of all its citizens. Welfare states aim to protect everyone from misfortune – anyone who falls ill or experiences problems, such as a sudden loss of income or of a home to live in. The classic idea of a welfare state was one of shared responsibility – or what is often referred to as *collective* responsibility – we all help each other out in times of need, relying mainly on government-run or -funded social services to do this: state schools, a health service, social care services, social housing for those who need it. Whether or not the government provides the services directly or pays private and voluntary sector organisations to provide them, if the state has promised to guarantee a certain standard of welfare for everyone it is still a welfare state. Income maintenance is the largest expenditure of a welfare state, usually in the form of cash benefits such as child and family benefits, Income Support, incapacity benefits and pensions.

Not all industrial or developed countries are welfare states. The USA and Japan, for example, are two affluent countries in which there are well-developed services, but these are not accessible to everyone on equal terms. In Japan, much depends on whether the *individual* can rely on the family or the employer; in the USA it is left to the *individual* to insure themselves against misfortune. It is this distinction between *individual* and *collective* responsibility that marks out welfare states from others.

1.1 Before the welfare state

Imagine what it would be like in the UK if there was no welfare state. In the next activity you will look back to the time in the UK before the welfare state and the protection it offers. Before the NHS the government ran a limited system of workers' health insurance. Workers' wives and children were not covered by this, however, and even the insured did not have cover from the state scheme for the cost of medicines or hospital care – only the cost of GP consultations was included.

Reader

Activity 2 Before the welfare state

Allow about 45 minutes

Turn to the Reader, Chapter 1, 'Anthology: people', compiled by Joanna Bornat and Ken Blakemore, and read Section 1.1, 'Personal recollections of the 20th century' (pages 5–10). As the title suggests, this contains some personal recollections of life during the earlier half of the twentieth century. These illustrate the social problems and welfare needs at that time. As you read through each one, put yourself in the shoes of the person remembering what happened to him or her. Then make a short note on each of the following questions:

(a) What happened when poor people were sick?

(b) What were the effects of the orphanage and the workhouse on family life?

(c) How did squalid housing conditions affect Edith Smith?

Comment

(a) When times were hard, people had to manage without medical care even if their needs were urgent or their illnesses life threatening. The case of the little girl dying of diphtheria illustrates this, as do the memories of David Taylor about the costs of obtaining medical treatments and having to rely on such things as lemonade to make you feel better.

(b) Although George Walter Cureton seemed to accept that it was necessary for him to be sent to an orphanage when his family moved to Birmingham, because there were no state benefits or allowances to support his widowed mother, by today's standards what happened to him would be seen as a heart-rending and wholly inappropriate solution that divided a family. Similarly, the threat of institutional care – the workhouse – hung over David Taylor's family. Not only would going into the workhouse from time to time have had a negative effect on his father's standing and sense of dignity, but there would also have been the underlying threat of the family being split up and the children being sent into children's homes or other institutions.

(c) Edith Smith's recollections illustrate the negative effects of poor housing on people's personal relationships and self-esteem. Her experience shows that in the 1930s a lot of unfit, unhealthy, pre-1914 housing remained, despite large increases in new housing in the 1920s and 1930s (Stevenson and Cook, 1994).

The lack of a basic, accessible health service was one important feature of life in Britain before the welfare state. But there were several other important factors that also help to explain why, in the 1930s, pressure was building for a better society. Perhaps the most important of these was the economic crisis of the time. Millions of workers had to be laid off work and the unemployment rate soared, particularly in the industrial areas of south Wales, northern England and central Scotland. Commonly, over a third of all workers were unemployed in these areas (Stevenson and Cook, 1994, pp. 65–6), and that led to the kinds of consequences you have been reading about.

The Jarrow Crusade: in October 1936, unemployed shipworkers from Jarrow in the north-east of England marched 300 miles to protest in London. Here, they are passing through Lavendon in Suffolk.

Hunger marchers passing through Gerrard's Cross, Buckinghamshire on their way to protest in London, October 1932

Unemployment and poverty were not hardships shared by everyone, however. The image of Britain in the 1930s is one of a divided society – one that continued to create great wealth, especially in areas of new industry in the Midlands and the south of England. Appalling squalor, disease and poverty in some parts of the country existed alongside a housing boom in the south and rising standards of living for many people who were in work.

The hardships and problems many people had to face in the 1920s and 1930s put pressure on government to provide better health and social welfare services. But by the 1930s people's *expectations* of a better life were rising too. The type of people campaigning for a better society included not only the 'have-nots' – the unemployed workers and the radical politicians who represented them – but also middle-class and professional people. For instance, a socialist-minded group of doctors campaigned for a national health service before the Second World War began in 1939 (Klein, 1989, pp. 2–10).

1.2 War: catalyst of the welfare state

The Second World War (1939–45) was a 'total war' involving the civilian population as well as the armed forces, and this common experience of total war forced the pace of change. Everyone was affected in some way. The Blitz (carpet bombing of towns and cities of Britain), food and fuel rationing, evacuation of children away from large urban centres, the blackout, government planning of wartime industries and the drive to get women into work – all these things transformed British society. Government regulation and control of nearly every detail of everyday life became 'normal'. Above all, this experience of war brought out a spirit of collective effort and forged a common sense of equality and citizenship. Few wanted to return to the pre-war conditions of the 1930s. The war generated mass public support for the sweeping social reforms and the introduction of a 'cradle-to-grave' welfare state that followed it.

A house in Surrey devastated by a German air raid in the Second World War. Shared misfortune forged a common sense of equality and citizenship.

During the war normal party politics – with one party in power and the others in opposition – were suspended and the country was governed by a coalition government led by Winston Churchill. Perhaps surprisingly, while waging all-out war this cross-party government began to make detailed plans for a new society after the war. In June 1941, less than two years into the war, the government appointed Sir William Beveridge, a well-known academic and specialist on employment and workers' welfare, to lead a committee that would look into the whole question of social insurance and social services.

In December 1942, only eighteen months after Beveridge was appointed, his report, *Social Insurance and Allied Services* was published. This report – the famous Beveridge Report – became the blueprint for the new post-war welfare state.

William Beveridge (1879–1963) in 1942

What was in the Beveridge Report?

Beveridge's report went far beyond tidying up the patchy and limited insurance schemes that existed at the time. He recommended a number of sweeping social reforms in addition to a much more comprehensive system of social security. His report represented a fundamental shift from seeing ill fortune as an *individual* concern to seeing it as a state or *collective* one that would ensure that all people were fit and well. As a consequence, the whole nation would benefit from increased productivity.

He argued that for his new social security system to work properly, the government would need to:

- Manage the economy so that there would be *full employment*. A job for everyone is the best way to eliminate poverty and its negative effects on health and well-being.
- Provide a *free national health service*. People shouldn't have to worry about insuring themselves against expensive medical bills.
- Pay *children's allowances* to every family with children, rich and poor alike. Not having a means test would guarantee that everyone who was eligible would be paid the benefit.

His social security scheme proposed a brand-new *state retirement pension*, and *sickness*, *unemployment*, *maternity* and *widows' benefits* as entitlements for everyone who was eligible.

In this way, Beveridge's plan seemed to be a radical break with the past because it was:

- a *universal* scheme covering everyone
- *unified* and simplified – people only had to pay into one fund to cover every benefit
- *not means tested* – benefits were paid *as of right*
- based on the idea of a *national minimum* – if someone was not on benefit or in receipt of a pension, the cost of their basic necessities (food, fuel and rent) would be covered
- a '*flat rate*' scheme – everyone paid in the same amount each week as everyone else and, if they needed to claim, they got the same amount in benefit as everyone else.

Beveridge wanted a better *education* system and *housing* for everyone, in addition to a new *health* service, *social security* for all and economic planning to generate *jobs*. Only in this way could what he saw as the five great social evils, or 'Giants' of Want, Ignorance, Disease, Squalor and Idleness be vanquished.

So how did the general public react to the publication of the Beveridge Report? And how much of a break with the past was it?

Reader

Activity 3 'A very British revolution'

Allow about 45 minutes

Read Chapter 25, 'An introduction to the Beveridge Report', by John Jacobs in the Reader (pages 215–21), which gives you some background on William Beveridge and includes a vivid account of the impact of his report. As Jacobs points out, Beveridge initially called his proposals 'revolutionary'. Later on, he qualified this by calling it a 'British revolution' – a 'natural development from the past'.

As you read the chapter, make a brief note on each of the following questions:

(a) Why was the report so popular with the general public?

(b) What was the difference between 'insurance' and 'assistance'?

(c) Jacobs identifies some groups who were not covered by the insurance scheme. Who were they?

Comment

(a) It is the underlying philosophy of the report that explains most of all why it had such wide appeal. The Beveridge Report held out the hope of a *fairer*, more *equal* and *socially just* world. The British experience of total war had had the effect of breaking down many of the pre-war class distinctions and differences. Beveridge's plan for a 'flat rate' system of social security meant that everyone would be treated the same way. On top of that, everyone would be entitled to a free secondary education and a free health service.

(b) Beveridge wanted all wage earners to contribute to a common insurance scheme – the term '*National Insurance*' dates from this time. It would mean that workers and their families would gain a sense of *dignity* and *self-respect*. There need be no shame about claiming a ('contributory') benefit, because you had a *right* to it – you had paid into the scheme and therefore deserved to draw on it when you needed to do so.

The *National Assistance* scheme was designed as a safety net for people unable to build up enough contributions to claim sufficient insurance benefits – young workers who become unemployed, for instance. Unlike National Insurance, however, National Assistance or 'the welfare', as it was called then, retained the taint of charity because it was *means tested* (i.e. people's 'means' or income had to be assessed, so that only those with incomes below a certain level could receive the benefit) and paid at a lower rate. However, Beveridge was convinced that with full employment, few people would need to fall back on it.

(c) The Beveridge plan was breathtakingly simple and radical for its time – the first universal social security system in the world. Having said that, a small number of people were *not* included – unmarried women carers not in work, single parents, and women who were divorced or separated from their husbands. As Jacobs points out, these were *relatively* small groups at the time. However, not including them proved to be a significant omission. Their numbers were to grow substantially in the post-war years – something that we will return to in Section 2.

This last point, about who was left out of the Beveridge scheme, raises a more general question – what were the limitations of the Beveridge plan? It might seem rather strange to be asking this question considering how positively it was regarded and its widespread acceptance as the best way to organise the post-war welfare state. But like every important social reform, the Beveridge Report was a product of its age. As Peter Hennessy puts it, it was 'as much backward looking (remedying past evils) as … forward looking (building a better tomorrow)' (Hennessy, 1992, p. 178). The Beveridge blueprint contained some significant drawbacks, which we will look at in the next section. They became increasingly evident in the post-war years and are still very relevant to health and social care now.

Key points

- In the 1930s, poverty, unemployment and growing dissatisfaction with inequality led to increasing pressure for better health care, social services and other improvements in living conditions.
- The Second World War was a catalyst for social reform and gave a sense of urgency to the need for an overhaul of the whole system of welfare.
- The Beveridge Report captured the mood for reform by proposing a universal system of social insurance, family allowances and a free health service for all.
- There was widespread public enthusiasm for Beveridge's plan and for the construction of a welfare state after the war.
- Despite its popularity at the beginning, Beveridge's scheme had some in-built limitations and drawbacks.

2 The Beveridge legacy: implications for care

As you saw earlier in the course, people needing care often experience financial hardship – either because they have just lost their livelihood or because they have been on a low income for a long time. For instance, right at the start of the course, in Unit 1, the point was made that informal carers are often poor and that caring makes them poorer. Angus McPhail and his carer Ann Walker both found that the benefits they could claim fell short of what they needed and wanted. The amount of Carer's Allowance that Ann could expect was surprisingly low. In this case, Ann was prepared to make sacrifices. She put her family obligations and her care for Angus first.

Arguably, this kind of situation has arisen partly because of the kind of welfare state that was constructed after the Second World War. In this section we will be looking at what happened after Beveridge's proposals were put into practice.

2.1 Building the welfare state, 1945–51

Most of Beveridge's proposals were adopted by the Labour government that won a landslide victory in the general election that took place in July 1945. Actually, two important elements in the 'welfare state package' were in place before the war ended. *Family Allowances* – later changed to Child Benefit – were introduced in 1944 by the coalition government. In the Education Act 1944 the wartime government also extended free *education* to the secondary level.

Between 1945 and 1951 the Labour government led by Clement Attlee set about implementing the rest of the Beveridge vision. In the next activity, take a look at the impressive list of social reforms that were introduced at this time.

6 August 1946: a mother and her family drawing her family allowance at Vicarage Lane Post Office, Stratford, East London, on the first day the allowance was paid

26 July 1945: British Prime Minister Clement Attlee, celebrating the Labour Party's landslide victory at the general election, with MP W.V. Edwards (left) and Mrs Attlee, in London

Activity 4 The coming of the welfare state

Allow about 5 minutes

The following list of legislation passed by the government between 1944 and 1949 represents a huge achievement. In just a few short years the main 'pillars' of the welfare state had been put in place. But was there a pillar missing? See if you can find any references to social care and social services legislation in the list of legislation below.

Education Act 1944: free secondary education for all.

National Insurance Act 1946: brought in National Insurance and entitlement to unemployment, sickness, maternity and widows' benefits, and the state pension.

National Health Service Act 1946 (implemented in July 1948): legislation to provide a free health service for all.

Children Act 1948: created local authority children's departments in local areas throughout the UK. Childcare officers were given the powers and duties necessary to take children into the care of the local authority.

National Assistance Act 1948: set up a National Assistance Board (the means-tested 'safety net' for anyone not covered by insurance benefits). It also required local authorities to promote the welfare of disabled people through the creation of local authority welfare departments and to provide accommodation for disabled, older and homeless people.

Housing Act 1949: provided for more public sector housing through local councils.

Comment

Did you note that, apart from the Children Act which related specifically to child welfare, the only legislation that dealt with social care was part of the National Assistance Act? Social care did not get its own special piece of legislation as a service of the welfare state *in its own right* in the way the NHS did.

Although the National Assistance Act was a major piece of legislation, it was not greeted with the same public fanfare and sense of achievement that ushered in the NHS. The very words 'National Assistance' conjured up associations with means-tested benefits and services to deal with 'problem people' – rather than being a mainstream service for all, like health and education.

These assumptions about social care, made by the architects of the welfare state, heralded what was to come – a rather neglected, 'Cinderella'-like role for the social services. We will come back to this point in Section 4.

To sum up, the welfare state that emerged into the daylight in the late 1940s was strikingly similar to the all-embracing plan with which Beveridge had caught the public imagination in 1942. At that time in Europe, only Britain and one other country, Sweden, stood out as welfare states based on the principle of *universalism* (see the box below).

Universalism

Universalism can be defined as the goal of making benefits and services (including health and social care) available to everyone, irrespective of a person's status or ability to pay.

The aim is to provide a universal service 'free' to everyone – paid for through taxation. In practice, some social services can only be provided with a means test, and those who can afford them have to pay. However, when we call a welfare state 'universal' this does imply that *as wide a range of services as possible* are provided 'free', or as heavily subsidised public services, to those who need them. Such services include social housing, community and leisure services, social security and education, as well as health and social care.

Highlight the definition in the first sentence in the box above, because in the next unit we will be exploring how this underlying principle of the welfare state has been modified.

2.2 Flaws in the post-war welfare state

The early 1950s was a period of austerity but also of economic growth and rising living standards. There was a general feeling that everyone should share in this post-war recovery. The Conservative government that followed Labour in 1951 continued with Beveridge's reforms, but already certain flaws were emerging.

Inadequate benefits and pensions

An increasing number of people on social security benefits and pensions found that what they were getting every week wasn't enough to make ends meet. They had to turn to means-tested National Assistance to survive. One of the main aims of Beveridge – to take away the means test – was already sinking into the sand. It looked as though benefit levels had been set too low.

This is the historical background to the hardships experienced by people in today's welfare state – people like Angus and Ann mentioned in Block 1. Beveridge established a tradition in Britain of setting benefits at a rather frugal, subsistence level. Although subsequent reforms lifted benefit levels substantially, in the UK they have never been raised to the levels enjoyed in other European countries, such as Germany, France and Sweden, where many benefits are more in line with average earnings.

Assumptions about gender roles

Another limitation of the 'Beveridgean' welfare state involves the assumptions made in the 1940s about the respective roles of men and women. These were apparent in the workforce, in the National Insurance scheme and in the home. In short, Beveridge has been criticised for being biased against women (by, for example, Lewis, 1983; Dale and Foster, 1986; Hallett, 1995).

At first sight this seems an unfair criticism. It would certainly have puzzled many women in the 1940s when the welfare state was introduced. After all, the welfare state helped women in many ways – for instance, by giving them a measure of financial independence through the provision of benefits such as family allowances, maternity benefits and widows' benefit. Other important benefits, such as the state retirement pension and unemployment benefit, were made available to women wage earners for the first time. In the 1940s and 1950s, many women felt that the scheme was an important advance for them, recognising them in public policy in a way that had not happened previously. Beveridge's own wife certainly took this view. In a book on the scheme published in 1954, Janet Beveridge commented that 'the whole joy of William's Scheme is its unconscious fairness to women' (Beveridge, 1954).

Let us look at what Beveridge actually said about the place of women in his scheme and the kind of reasoning he used. He gave considerable attention to the position of married women:

> … the great majority of married women must be regarded as occupied on work which is vital though unpaid, without which their husbands could not do their paid work and without which the nation could not continue.
>
> (Beveridge, 1942, p. 49, para. 107)

This 'vital work' comprised a number of things. It included women caring for their husbands and children and maintaining the home. Also, as you will know from studying this course, it often involved being what is now called an informal carer, looking after chronically ill or disabled parents or other family members. For Beveridge, however, the main component of married women's vital work was producing and caring for children. Note that in Beveridge's eyes, a key reason to encourage motherhood and to maintain a good supply of healthy children was to support the work of the British Empire – an imperialist view that was still widely shared at the time. He stated:

> The attitude of the housewife to gainful employment outside the home is not and should not be the same as that of a single woman. She has other duties …
>
> In the next thirty years housewives as mothers have vital work to do in ensuring the adequate continuance of the British race and of British ideals in the world.
>
> (Beveridge, 1942, p. 51, para. 114; p. 53, para. 117)

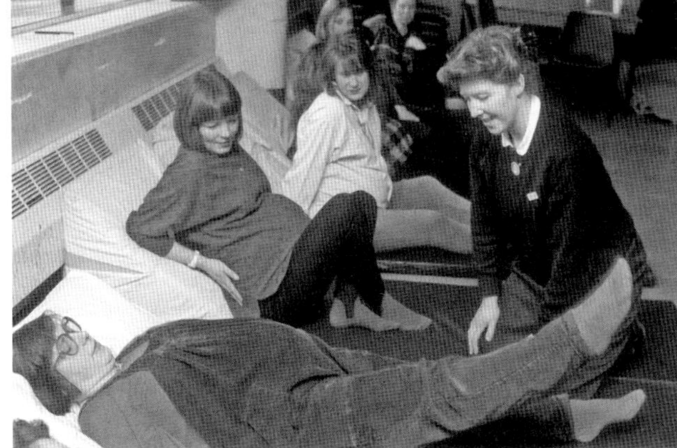

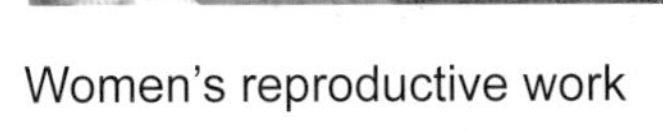

Women's reproductive work

It was because of his acknowledgement of the importance of childbearing and childcare that Beveridge felt that married women should be entitled to economic support from their husbands, both for themselves and for their children. He went further and advocated maternity benefit at a level higher than unemployment benefit. This was altered after a few years, but was an indication of the importance he attached to women's 'vital work' in the home.

Single women could take part on the same footing as single men in the insurance scheme. And while Beveridge assumed that women would probably not remain in paid work after they got married, if they *did* choose to work outside the home they had the option of making National Insurance contributions if they wanted to. Women who paid their own contributions received lower benefits than employed men in return for lower contributions. The reasoning was that women were deemed not to have the main responsibility for upkeep of the home – paying the rent, for instance, was assumed to be the male breadwinner's responsibility.

Activity 5 Fair to women? Fair to men?

Allow about 15 minutes

Read once more the quotations from the Beveridge Report given above. Now jot down your answers to the following questions:

(a) In what ways might Beveridge's approach be considered fair to women?

(b) In what ways might Beveridge's scheme be considered unfair to women?

(c) Did men get a better deal than women?

Comment

(a) A case can be made for saying that the Beveridge Report was fair to women. But perhaps the case only holds water if you adopt the standards and outlook of the 1940s. Beveridge recognised that:

- women of the time had a different place from men in society, and made provision for it
- what women did in the home was important work, and men's economic activity could not take place without it
- women were an integral part of the scheme and their different needs were recognised
- married women should be given a choice as to whether they wanted to opt in or out of the scheme.

(b) There is no doubt that in other respects Beveridge was unfair to women:

- He did not treat the two sexes equally. Married women did not have the opportunity to contribute and benefit in the same way as men (even if they contributed to the scheme, their benefits would be lower).
- Married women were seen not as individual contributors in their own right, but as wives. The scheme made them dependants of their husbands and effectively locked them into marriage.
- Family allowances apart, women were not given any financial recompense for their vital work; their choices about doing or not doing caring work of all kinds were restricted.

(c) Men were handed more economic privileges by the scheme and seemed to be treated as the superior sex. But the male breadwinner role was restrictive in many ways:

- It encouraged the idea that men were there to 'look after' their wives and children. Yet there were always some men who failed to do this very well, or to do it at all – sometimes as a result of chronic illness, but also because they were feckless or incompetent.
- Where men wanted to play a bigger part in raising their families, however, the 'male breadwinner' role proved to be restrictive. Just as women were treated as wives who were expected to stay at home, so men were expected to go out to work. Some studies have shown how the social security system is usually much more active or coercive in encouraging young men into paid work than it is women with young children (Hasluck, 2000; Hetherington, 2000).

As the social and cultural changes of the 1960s and 1970s began to affect the roles of women and men, the assumptions that Beveridge had made in the early 1940s about gender roles looked increasingly out of date; he had not anticipated the rapid rise in the divorce rate after the late 1960s. However, Beveridge had initially suggested an allowance or benefit for separated and divorced wives. He was reluctantly persuaded to drop this proposal, though, because of the argument that benefits for divorced and separated women would be seen as 'subsidising sin' (Thane, 1982, p. 249).

The kind of welfare system set up after the Second World War was therefore geared to traditional family structures rather than the realities of family life that emerged later in the twentieth century. In addition to neglecting single parents and divorced women, we saw earlier (in Activity 3) how the Beveridge scheme excluded other groups. Many unmarried women, for instance, stayed at home to look after their parents. Not being wage earners meant that these women could not claim National Insurance benefits in their own right. Similarly, many disabled people could not be included in the scheme because they were not wage earners.

Thus, the Beveridge welfare state, based on the idea of financial protection through a compulsory insurance scheme, had its limitations. But now, in the next section, we can start to look at what the welfare state legislation of the 1940s led to in terms of actual *services*.

Key points

- The immediate post-war social legislation set the scene for social care becoming the poor relation of health care.
- The welfare state was based on assumptions of continuing high employment and a stable family unit.
- Benefits and pensions were set at a relatively low, 'subsistence' level, with the result that they proved inadequate to prevent poverty and a return to means-tested benefits on a large scale.
- The Beveridge vision relied on limited gender roles: married women were expected to provide care in the home and their husbands to go out to work.
- Single women providing care at home were undervalued by the welfare state.

3 The new National Health Service

In the last section we looked at how the welfare state was created. Now we are going to look at what happened afterwards. In this section we look at the period from 1948 to 1979, focusing first of all on health care. In the next section we will consider social care and social services.

Alongside the new National Insurance scheme it was the NHS that became the jewel in the crown of the welfare state. In many respects, the NHS, introduced on 5 July 1948, has proved to be a great success. It is a unique service. No other comparable industrial country has such a comprehensive health service provided free at the point of use. It enshrines the welfare state values underpinning all the other major reforms of the 1940s: equality, fairness and compassion. And despite its acknowledged shortcomings, it remains popular with the public.

3.1 A compromise with the doctors

Aneurin Bevan: architect of the new NHS

Some kind of comprehensive medical service had been under discussion before the Second World War, and after the war Aneurin Bevan, Labour's Health Minister, was determined to nationalise Britain's creaking health care system. No longer was health care going to be left to private enterprise (private health care for those who could afford it) or to charity hospitals or the variable municipal hospitals. The state was going to provide all the necessary health services for everyone, on the same basis.

However, the government could not achieve these aims without the support of the powerful medical profession. Many doctors were opposed in principle to Bevan's plan because the British Medical Association (BMA) favoured the idea of an expanded health service based on medical insurance.

Between 1946 and 1948, a hard-fought contest took place between the doctors and the Ministry of Health (Klein, 1989, pp. 20–5). The doctors' opposition almost wrecked the government's plans – even though they had been agreed by Parliament in the 1946 National Health Service Act. As Rudolf Klein describes, it was a 'real cliff-hanger'. The doctors held out for as many concessions as they could get from the government. Aneurin Bevan came up with a deal for the consultants – the medical elite – to pay them substantial 'merit awards' for achievements in medical research and practice, on top of their salaries – a reward system that is still in place today. Bevan admitted that he had had to 'stuff their mouths with gold' to stop their opposition (Fraser, 1984, p. 235).

Finally, in the spring of 1948, the British Medical Association agreed to a structure with which they felt they could work – and, basically, this is the structure of the NHS and health care that we have today.

That's why this story is important, not just for the record but because it helps to explain why medical power was – and still is – so dominant in the NHS. In a nutshell, Britain was presented with a state health service in July 1948, but *not* a state-run health service. Central government was going to control the purse strings, but it was going to let the doctors have the biggest say in all the major decisions – how to run the new health services, where to spend the money, what the priorities for the future would be. The NHS was to begin its life as a state organisation steered by a profession – the medical profession.

3.2 The three arms of the NHS

The structure of the NHS that the government and the doctors signed up to is best described as having three parts or 'arms' – what can also be described as a 'tripartite' structure. Each of the three main components of the NHS was designed to work rather separately from the others. The three arms were:

- hospital services
- GPs or family practitioner services
- local authority or community health services.

Hospital services

This arm took the lion's share of the health budget from government. After the state take-over in 1948, hospitals were grouped together in local areas. They were overseen by hospital management committees (in which doctors had the most influence), which reported to regional hospital boards (also dominated by the medical profession) and thence to the Minister of Health. High-status teaching hospitals in London and other big cities jealously guarded their autonomy. They managed to keep their own boards of governors and a direct line to the Minister. Hospital doctors agreed to become salaried employees of the NHS on condition that consultants were allowed to run private practices in NHS hospitals.

The NHS inherited a large network of hospitals providing long-term care for people with mental health problems and 'mental handicaps' – hospitals that resembled Lennox Castle, which was featured in Block 2. The NHS also took on some local 'cottage hospitals' and nursing homes. None of these facilities was its top priority. Robin Means and Randall Smith (1994) refer to a history of neglect and poor-quality care in long-stay hospitals for those who were mentally ill, physically disabled, frail and old. By way of example, the following quotation, from an interview with Dr Samuel Vine who later became one of the pioneers of the new specialty of geriatric medicine, illustrates the situation in the early days of the NHS:

> [Dr S] said 'Oh look, there's one frightful little chore that you have to do. I'm awfully sorry but somewhere … I've never been in them, of course, but … there are what are called the chronic sick wards … all you've got to do is find an hour or so on an alternate Thursday afternoon, just pop in there, have a word with the sister, see if there's anything she wants, it's mainly repeating prescriptions, I think that's all you have to do. Don't let it interfere with … I'm sorry about it, old boy.'
>
> And so the first Thursday came along and I found these dreadful wards. …
>
> Well, I was shocked, amazed, appalled, saddened and very upset at what I saw that afternoon. I could not believe that … within the campus of one hospital, two separate standards should exist for treatment based solely upon age, 65 for men and 60 for women. … and I thought 'Well, I'm going to stop this' and I said 'Now how do people get into here? I can't do anything about these you've got but I shall do something about those that are coming under my care … How do they get here?' And do you know how they got there? A waiting list subscribed to by GPs outside who thought they had somebody who perhaps ought to spend their days in hospital. The name and address was given willy-nilly to the sister in charge of the casualty department, who just kept it as a register and as one died – that was the only way you were discharged from these

wards – as one died the next on the list was sent for irrespective of need with no prior assessment and nothing further about it.

It's unbelievable, isn't it?

(*Oral History of Geriatrics as a Speciality*, Dr Samuel Vine interviewed by Anthea Holme, 1991)

Family practitioner services

Family practitioner services included mainly GPs (general practitioners, or family doctors), but also dentists and opticians. These three groups were determined not to be direct NHS employees. They remained as independent contractors to the NHS. GPs worked on their own or in groups, loosely coordinated by a number of executive councils. Thus, GP practices started out in the NHS as small independent businesses and have stayed as businesses right through to the present time. Most are now much bigger enterprises than they were in the 1940s. They have taken on a bigger administrative and commissioning role in primary care trusts (PCTs).

Local authority health services

Every city and county council retained its own health committees and medical officers of health, and these too became part of the new NHS. Local authorities were responsible for public health – much of what we now call 'environmental health'. But they also controlled a number of community-based preventive services: school medical and nursing services, district nursing, health visiting, home helps, maternity and child welfare clinics, and child guidance clinics. And, through local authority mental health departments, they ran certain preventive and aftercare services for what was known at the time as 'mental illness' and 'mental defectiveness'.

This organisational structure lasted for the first twenty-five years of the NHS in England and Wales, although the position in Scotland and Northern Ireland differed somewhat, and still does.

Activity 6 The three arms of the NHS

Allow about 10 minutes

Designing the NHS with three separate 'arms' had a certain logic at the time and the design was approved by the medical profession. However, there were drawbacks. Can you think of any? Write down at least one, and another if you can think of any more.

Comment

You might have spotted that, because they were separate arms, coordination between them would be tricky.

For example, GPs provided a medical service for the local community that tended to work rather separately from nurses and other health services, which were run by the local authority. Staff on hospital wards needed to be sure that a district nursing service or a bed in a residential home would be available for discharged patients, but there was not much they could do to press for more resources or for services to be organised differently.

These kinds of issues have not gone away and pleas for better integration of services continue to be heard today. If you have worked in the NHS or have special knowledge of it, you might also have suggested some of the additional points noted below.

3.3 A 'National Sickness Service'?

A single phrase to sum up how the NHS developed between the 1950s and the 1970s would be 'hospital-centred health care'. As a result, much of the energy and investment in these decades went into dealing with *illness* in hospitals rather than into promoting or maintaining people's *health* through preventive work or other measures – hence the view that the NHS was becoming a 'National Sickness Service' or a 'National Hospital Service'. As Steve Taylor and David Field explain, it was generally assumed that expert care by doctors in hospitals was the route to better health:

> This led to the expectation that it was only a matter of time before scientific medicine overcame the diseases of modern society, such as cancer, heart disease, arthritis and mental illness. It was widely anticipated in industrial societies around the middle of the twentieth century that much greater investment in medical research and health care would produce further dramatic improvements in levels of health.
>
> (Taylor and Field, 2003, p. 22)

The NHS was undoubtedly the rational solution of its time for trying to provide the best medical services available as fairly and equally as possible. But the NHS was reinforcing the medical hierarchy (Klein, 1989, p. 21). Doctors had won the right to take the lead in managing the bodies responsible for the health service. Local authority representation on these bodies was reduced to a minimum, and no other health professions were represented at this early stage, as Klein explains (1989, p. 21). Thus, doctors gained through the NHS what Field describes as 'a near monopoly' of the right to treat the sick. Nurses, for instance, were incorporated into the NHS 'subordinated to medical control and their activities largely delegated to them with little scope for autonomy' (Field, 2003, p. 191).

Field (2003) discusses other effects of the medical hierarchy on the NHS. Working as a consultant or a doctor in mental health or geriatric medicine was not as glamorous as being a specialist in chest and heart surgery, for instance. There was no merit award and little scope for private practice either; long-stay hospitals became the backwaters of the NHS. And doctors who went into general practice were seen as less successful in their medical careers compared with hospital doctors and consultants. Putting acute care in hospitals on a pedestal also had effects on those parts of health care that remained with the local authorities. The job of medical officer of health had a much lower status than that of a hospital clinician working with individual patients.

Although GPs had less status in the medical hierarchy, they played a pivotal gatekeeper role in the NHS, and continue to do so. There is no direct equivalent elsewhere to the GP role found in the UK. In many other countries, health care systems provide for direct access to specialists. The main advantage of the way the GP service was set up in the British NHS was its ease of access. Almost everyone in the UK could register with a GP practice. Most practices were within easy reach of home or work and there was no charge for a GP consultation. However, lack of financial incentives to spend time with patients and difficulties of coordination with other community-based health services, run by the local authority, meant that

GPs would remain, primarily, gatekeepers of the 'National Sickness Service' rather than developing a national, community-based preventive service.

So much for the structure of the new health service, but how was it to be staffed?

3.4 The role of health care professionals from overseas

The first eight years or so in the life of the NHS were a period of consolidation. The health service's 'plant' – its hospitals and other facilities – was mostly outdated and pre-war. There was little money for expansion: the British economy was struggling to its feet after the disruption of the Second World War. Also, it took time for everyone employed in the NHS to get used to the new arrangements. Before long, however, the NHS began to grow and, by the 1970s, the UK's NHS had become the largest single employer in the whole of Western Europe.

How was this vast state enterprise staffed? As demand for people to work in the NHS began to grow from 1955 on, a rising proportion of new staff were drawn from overseas. As David Owen explains (2003, pp. 23–4), the key reason was a general shortage of labour in Britain in the 1950s and 1960s, a period of economic expansion and reconstruction. Nurses were recruited from the Caribbean and from south-east Asian countries, primarily Malaysia and the Philippines. Doctors tended to come from India, Pakistan and a range of African countries. There is no doubt that the NHS faced a serious labour shortage and that health workers from overseas were needed and energetically sought (McNaught, 1988, p. 46).

The number of overseas doctors working in the NHS grew rapidly in the 1960s and 1970s. By 1978 over a third of all hospital doctors, a fifth of all GPs and a fifth of those working in community and school health services had been born overseas, with many of these coming from African and Asian countries and from Ireland (McNaught, 1988, p. 39). Also, by the late 1970s, a substantial proportion of practising midwives in the UK – again well over a third – had been recruited from overseas countries (McNaught, 1988, p. 39).

By the end of the 1970s, then, migrant health care workers and professionals had become an integral part of the health service. The NHS had developed both a multinational and a multiracial workforce: in doing this it was reflecting the steady globalisation of the labour market for health care work. And although the NHS did provide some training and further opportunities for nurses and doctors from overseas, it had also been able to gain from the training that these migrant health workers had already been given in their home countries. In effect, there was a net transfer to the UK of resources spent on training in poorer countries, such as Ghana, Nigeria, India and Pakistan (where there were severe shortages of doctors and nurses).

One of the features of this pattern of migration, as Aneez Esmail (2007) points out, was that although the majority of doctors wanted to work in teaching hospitals, so that they could develop their skills in acute medicine and surgery, this option was rarely available. Rather, black and Asian doctors and nurses were over-represented in the less popular specialties for older people, people with mental health problems and people with long-term impairments, and under-represented in the more prestigious areas of medicine (McNaught, 1988, p. 39). Furthermore, those black and Asian doctors who ended up in general practice were more likely to be found in the more deprived areas of Britain, often well away from the prestigious hospitals (Taylor and Esmail, 1999).

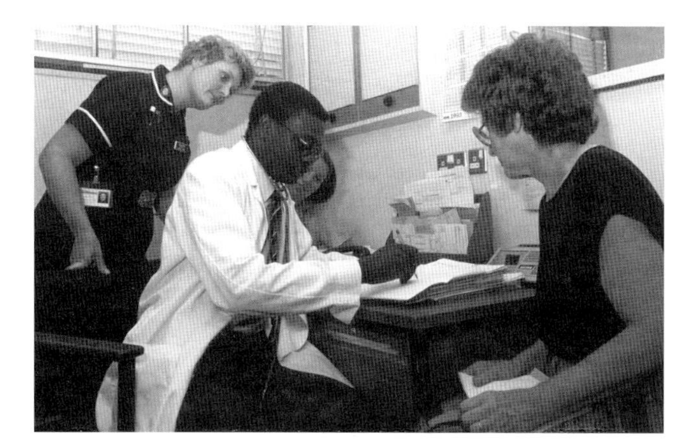

The contribution of 'overseas' doctors and nurses to the NHS remains as important today as it was in the past

A second feature was that migrant workers in the NHS had relatively little success in attaining senior positions or professional acclaim. Mares et al. (1985) explain how, in the 1960s and early 1970s, most overseas nurses were channelled into state enrolled nurse (SEN) training rather than the higher-ranking state registered nurse (SRN) qualification: 'by 1972, 9 per cent of all NHS nurses came from overseas, but they [made up] 20 per cent of the total of SENs working in the NHS' (Mares et al., 1985, p. 159). Esmail and colleagues found that doctors from minority ethnic groups were less likely than white doctors to receive distinction or discretionary awards (Esmail et al., 1998, 2003).

Reader

Activity 7 Thwarted ambitions?

Allow about 15 minutes

Turn again to the Reader, Chapter 1, 'Anthology: people', compiled by Joanna Bornat and Ken Blakemore, and read Section 1.3, 'The Caribbean contribution to the NHS' (pages 11–12). Here you will find brief accounts of the experiences of Dr Moonsawmy and Dr Franklyn Jacobs. After you have done this, read through again the last two paragraphs above. Then note down why you think the ambitions of black and Asian doctors and nurses who migrated from overseas were often thwarted.

Comment

According to researchers, including those mentioned above, racial and ethnic discrimination – both deliberate and unwitting – played a big part in limiting opportunities for black and minority ethnic staff in the NHS. Dr Moonsawmy's account also points to the prejudice he encountered from the general public.

The fact that racial discrimination has a long history in the NHS is borne out by a string of industrial tribunal cases which investigated complaints by black and other minority ethnic staff in the late 1970s and 1980s (McNaught, 1988, pp. 41–4). These landmark cases revealed, among other things, 'poor interviewing and selection procedures' and 'crude racial discrimination (for instance in the case of University College Hospital [who] were "not keen to employ black staff")' (McNaught, 1988, pp. 43–4).

There were other barriers to the career development of migrant workers. For example, overseas-trained doctors were less likely to have had the opportunity to work in a British teaching hospital, so they were more likely to miss out on the informal networks associated with working in those hospitals, which influenced entry into certain specialties (Smith, 1980).

It could be argued, therefore, that through racial and ethnic discrimination, the NHS succeeded in keeping black and Asian staff in the positions that indigenous doctors and health workers were less willing to take. However, although this may be true, it is important not to lose sight of the fact that overcoming the kinds of barriers to career development identified above represents an immense achievement, both for individual migrants and collectively. The brief accounts from Dr Moonsawmy and Dr Franklyn Jacobs are testimony to this.

However, the disquieting record of prejudice and discrimination in the NHS prompts further questions about its good and bad points.

3.5 Evaluating the NHS

During the 1960s, it became increasingly obvious that the NHS had a number of serious problems, not only in relation to costs but also with its structure and the way in which resources were being allocated between different parts of the service. As we have seen, for example, resources tended to move towards the hospital sector at the expense of the family doctor and community health services. Also, resources were shared unequally among the hospitals and the regions. Another complication was that the hospital regions varied widely in size and needs.

A better way had to be found of providing a free, equal and affordable NHS – but how? The story of the NHS is basically a story of the search by successive governments for a solution to this question. Before we go any further, however, let's take stock. Activity 8 will help you to consolidate your understanding of 'what kind of animal' the UK's health service is – and why it throws up problems as well as being admired as one of the best health care systems in the world.

Activity 8 The NHS: pros and cons

Allow about 30 minutes

Section 3 has been dealing with the story of how the NHS developed. A paradox about the NHS, as we pointed out at the beginning of this section, is that, despite its many shortcomings, it remains popular with the public.

Look back over this section and note down the weaknesses in how the NHS was designed and developed. Then, drawing on your own experience as a health service user, note down why you think the NHS has remained so popular.

Comment

Some of the weaknesses in the way the NHS was designed and has developed, which we have identified in this section, include:

- hospital-centred at expense of community and preventive services
- GPs controlling access to specialist treatment

- acute sector better funded than long-stay
- some specialties more prestigious than others
- separation of health and social care
- hierarchical workforce dominated by consultants
- history of racial discrimination in the workforce
- lack of democratic accountability
- private practice within the NHS leading to a two-tier service
- uneven quality of the services provided across the country.

Despite these weaknesses, the NHS is based on the principle of *equality* and is open and *accessible* to all. It employs a highly trained *professional* workforce and most of its services are *free*. You might want to conclude that having a free National Health Service outweighs any number of disadvantages. On the other hand, it is important to be aware of the costs and drawbacks of having a health service like the NHS, even though we might want to hang on to its key principle of aiming to provide free health care to all.

In the 1970s, both Conservative and Labour governments had recognised that reform of the NHS was needed. It seemed particularly important to organise a better way of planning the health service as a whole – setting priorities and getting a more strategic vision of how the various parts of the NHS could work together. In 1974, there was a breakthrough when a major reform of the structure was implemented. The medical profession was to retain a very important role in management, but would work in a more centrally managed organisation. Also, the lack of democratic input into running the NHS was to be tackled. New advisory committees to health authorities were introduced, along with community health councils to represent patients and other interest groups.

The overhaul of the NHS in the 1970s was the first major shake-up the health service had experienced since it was created. However, one particular problem was left largely untouched. This was the separation of health and social care – a drawback that had been built into the original design in the 1940s.

Key points

- The NHS was shaped by powerful medical interests in the acute hospitals.
- It introduced a tripartite structure in England and Wales, which was difficult to coordinate. In effect, it meant the dominance of hospital-centred health care.
- The NHS recruited substantial numbers of migrant health workers, but there was widespread racial discrimination against them, both in their initial appointments and in further training and promotion opportunities.
- There have been efforts to reform the NHS in order to resolve some its structural problems.
- The separation of health and social care is one problem that has not been resolved.

4 Social care: the poor relation

We have just looked at how the NHS developed between the early 1950s and the 1970s. How does the story of social care and social services compare?

4.1 The legacy of the Poor Law

To start, let's take a look in the next activity at the account of Cecil French, who was appointed in 1946 to work in the mental health department of a local authority. He paints a vivid picture of the limitations of the community mental health service in the late 1940s and 1950s.

Activity 9 Care standards in a 'Cinderella' service

Allow about 10 minutes

Read Cecil French's account below and then note down a brief answer to each of these questions:

(a) What scale of mental welfare service was available to people in the community?

(b) What was the role of institutional care in those days?

(c) In addition to the reason Cecil French gives, can you think of other reasons why some people who needed care were 'kept in a back room'?

> As far as the mentally ill were concerned one dealt with them by admission to hospital. There was no other way. As for subnormals, there were four of us to cover the whole county. We each had 350 to 400 cases so that they were very fortunate if they got two visits a year. We used to aim at one and a quarter, but that didn't ever come off. We didn't have the time. Of course in the early days the presence of a mentally handicapped child was frequently hidden and you didn't know the child existed. There were quite a number of people who were kept in a back room, and it was not uncommon for, if anything happened to an elderly father or mother, all of a sudden this pale face came out of the woodwork. There was nothing for them, you see. Unless they got really desperate and the family at home couldn't cope any more then they came to us of necessity to get into hospital. There wasn't any point coming forward, because we had nothing to offer.
>
> (Interview with Cecil French by Jan Walmsley, October 1991)

Comment

(a) Although Beveridge's 'cradle-to-grave' welfare state and the NHS were hailed as great achievements, Cecil French's account shows that in the 1950s help barely existed for the people in the community with whom he was dealing – children with learning disabilities and people with mental and physical impairments living with their families.

(b) These were the days when a much higher proportion of those people diagnosed with mental health problems, or as 'mentally ill' in the language of the time, were 'taken away' than are today – sometimes for years on end.

In some cases they were lost to their families forever. The boundary between family care and institutional care was very sharp. Back then, it was either an institutional solution or staying at home to be looked after by the family. There was little or no intermediate provision by health or social services for people with mental health problems or long-term disabilities.

(c) Not only would there be nothing for them from the care services, as Cecil French explains, but asking for help for a child with a learning disability, or a 'mental handicap', could result in embarrassment and fear. First, they would have to admit that there was 'an odd one in the family'. In an age when social attitudes were very prejudiced as far as disability and mental illness were concerned, this was seen as shameful. Second, there would be loss of pride in having to admit that the family could not cope without help from 'the welfare'. Third, hanging over all this there was often real fear in families that their child would be 'put away'.

Cecil French's account indicates just how close parts of the welfare state still were to the old Poor Law days and how the welfare services were dominated by institutional provision.

The Poor Law

The Poor Laws have historical roots that go back centuries. In the nineteenth century, earlier methods of providing assistance to the poor and destitute were reformed. Previously, many local districts had developed a way of helping the poor by giving them an allowance of bread or money (the dole), which was paid for by a local tax (the rates) on property holders. Being in receipt of the dole meant that many poor families could just about survive and were able to stay in their own homes. In 1834, a Poor Law Act brought in a tougher, more hard-headed approach. The main aim was to deter people from seeking public assistance (from the parish) and to reduce the cost of paying for 'poor relief'. The process of seeking help was deliberately made as harsh, discouraging and demeaning an experience as possible. The 1834 Act did this by restricting help to those who had been reduced to total destitution – labelled 'paupers' – and by requiring anyone who was to receive help to enter a sex-segregated workhouse, thus splitting up families and parents (although in practice only a minority of paupers were institutionalised because the cost of building a sufficiently large number of workhouses proved to be too great). Later on, the Poor Law workhouse system developed into a set of more specialised and separate institutions run by local authorities – for instance, asylums for the 'mentally ill' and 'mentally defective', orphanages and children's homes, municipal hospitals and approved schools for young offenders. Although the last vestiges of the Poor Law were formally abolished in 1948, the shame and fear associated with being 'put away' in a local authority institution lasted for decades afterwards.

4.2 The 1950s and 1960s: a fragmented service

The provision of social work and social care services in the 1950s and 1960s was provided in part by the local authority health committees, mentioned in the last section, and in part by newly created welfare departments.

- *Mental health departments*, employing mental welfare officers, such as Cecil French, were set up under the National Health Service Act 1946 to provide community care for people who were 'mentally ill' or 'defective' and to convey people to hospital under the Lunacy Act 1890 and the Mental Treatment Act 1930. As you saw earlier, in Activity 4, apart from the National Health Service Act 1946, two other pieces of legislation by the post-war Labour government were particularly important for the development of social care – the Children Act 1948 and the National Assistance Act 1948.
- Through the Children Act, new local authority *children's departments*, staffed by childcare officers, were set up. The aim was to provide a service for the care of children who had not had the benefit of a 'normal' home life.
- The National Assistance Act, in addition to providing means-tested monetary support for people who didn't qualify for National Insurance benefits, also established new *welfare departments* in local authorities. These departments were given a duty 'to promote the welfare of persons who are blind, deaf or dumb and others who are substantially and permanently handicapped by illness, injury or congenital deformity'. One section of the Act required them to provide residential accommodation for older people and, as you will recall from the list we used in Activity 4, there were also responsibilities to provide accommodation for homeless people.
- In addition to these three departments, other welfare services were provided by local authority *education departments*, which employed education welfare officers; *housing departments*, which employed housing welfare officers; and *health departments*, which employed home helps and child guidance workers. Furthermore, medical social workers were employed in *hospitals*.

In summary, the responsibility to provide what we now call social work and social care services was spread across a range of local authority departments. On the face of it, this was promising. In practice, however, it was much less so. The development of services to support people in their own homes in the 1950s and 1960s was slow and patchy, and many with severe needs, as you saw in Cecil French's description, were left in the community without adequate services. Exactly what was available depended on where you lived and what your needs were. Looking back on what were called 'domiciliary services' to support people at home, Means and Smith conclude:

> … domiciliary services were an 'extra frill' and could be left to voluntary organisations … A complex patchwork of visiting services, day centres, meals services and chiropody did emerge but much of this provision was unevenly spread geographically.
>
> (Means and Smith, 1994, p. 25)

Although domiciliary or home care grew slowly in the 1950s and 1960s, there was an increasing awareness of the spiralling cost of residential and hospital care services which continued to dominate care provision. The critics of institutional care were gathering force. Advocates of a shift towards providing care services in people's homes were gaining ground:

> … for example, in the 1950s a Royal Commission studied the care of 'the mentally handicapped' and proposed living arrangements in community settings; the 1959 Mental Health Act sought to establish community care for the mentally ill, and this led to a significant reduction in long-stay hospital facilities, especially in the old Victorian asylums … [and] in 1963, the Conservative government produced a White Paper on the development of community care (Cmnd 1973).
>
> (Blakemore, 1998, p. 167)

While some worried about the mounting financial cost of care in institutions, others were concerned about the human cost of institutional care. This is something you studied in Blocks 2 and 4 and in particular in the work of Erving Goffman (1961). Goffman was one of several researchers in the 1960s who mounted a strong critique of institutions and their impact on people's lives. Another of the critics you read about in Block 4 was Peter Townsend who, in his study *The Last Refuge* (1962), reported that much of the residential accommodation for older people inherited by the new welfare departments was from the days of the Poor Law, with the same buildings and the same staff. This accommodation was a last refuge because, for many residents, there was no choice but to accept it. For most, however, any other solution would have been preferable, but these were the people without family to look after them or enough money to pay for a better type of care.

Given this questioning of long-stay hospital and residential care from all sides, it was not surprising that towards the end of the 1960s there was mounting pressure to start closing down the larger institutions. At the same time, if community-based care was to become a reality, there had to be some rethinking about how social services outside those institutions should be provided and organised.

Peter Townsend, in his book *The Last Refuge*, reported that over three-fifths of older people in residential care in the late 1950s were still being accommodated in ex-public assistance institutions like this one in Wolverhampton (now demolished)

4.3 Seebohm: a universal service?

These changes in thinking were an important part of the background to taking the next big step – the reorganisation of social services in 1971 as set out in the Seebohm Report of 1968. Frederic Seebohm's brief was to conduct a general inquiry into the 'shortcomings of the present social services' and to recommend ways of improving the 'co-ordination, quality, range and amount' of local authority service provision (Seebohm, 1968, p. 29). So what did he recommend and how would his proposals affect people requiring social services? We will explore this question in the next activity.

Punch depicts the Seebohm Report as offering a 'welfare umbrella' for people of all ages

Activity 10 The effect of the Seebohm Report

Allow about 20 minutes

Read through the box below, which briefly outlines the main changes recommended by Seebohm. Then think about someone you know or have come across in K101, such as Jordan whose life story book you looked at in Block 2, or Ann and Angus whose stories you heard in Block 1. Try to imagine how their needs might have been met by the welfare services in the 1950s and 1960s. Make a few notes on who might have visited them. Then note down the difference that Seebohm's proposed reorganisation would make for them.

The Seebohm Report 1968

Seebohm recommended the following.

A unified department

A unified 'social services department' would take over the work previously carried out by the mental health, welfare and children's departments. The new department would also take over the work of education and housing welfare officers and the home help service. It would, in effect, become a fifth social service alongside health, education, social security and housing, attracting substantial resources.

Employing social workers with 'generic' skills

The various professional groups – mental welfare officers, for example – were to lose their separate identities to become 'social workers'. Social workers could still specialise in particular areas of work, but they would be trained to acquire a general (*generic*) range of skills. Social work would therefore become a unified profession of generic practitioners, rather than having workers specialising solely in mental health, childcare, and so on.

A universal family and community service

Seebohm envisaged a service for everyone, not just 'the poor' or particular groups of 'social casualties'. Chiming with this was the proposal to make community work and community development a central part of the work of the local authority social services department. Again, the goal was to develop preventive services for the whole community rather than a service that was limited to 'picking up the pieces' with individuals and families.

Comment

Given the range of challenges facing Jordan, his step-sister, mother and grandmother, his various foster parents and his schoolteachers, there was clearly potential for a variety of welfare workers to be involved. For example, it is possible that Jordan may have had contact with a childcare officer, a child guidance worker and an education welfare officer, while his mother, in addition, may have been visited by the housing welfare and the mental welfare officers.

Seebohm's proposal for a 'single door' or point of access to all kinds of services represented a very big change from the way in which social services had been organised up to that point. Clients such as Jordan's mother, who had a number of requirements, would no longer have to trek from one department to another. The system would be simpler to understand and she would be able to deal with one designated social worker for all issues affecting the family.

Furthermore, Seebohm's aim to develop a service that, through community work, would help to *prevent* social, family and personal problems from occurring might at least have prevented Jordan's difficulties from becoming so serious.

Seebohm's vision of transforming the personal social services into the fifth great 'social service' of the welfare state, equal in scale and importance to the other four – the NHS, social security, education and housing – was the biggest chance for the social services since 1948 to leave behind their 'Cinderella' status.

The social context also favoured change. The 1960s was an optimistic, confident decade. It was a less complicated, 'public sector' world – certainly a world away from the 1980s when privatisation and a market in social services began to be considered. The Seebohm Committee was confident about the ability of the state and the public sector – in the form of the local authorities – to carry out the necessary reforms and expansion of social services.

Legislation followed the recommendations of the Seebohm Report in the form of the Local Authority Social Services Act 1970. The big shake-up of social services began in England and Wales in 1971. Coincidentally, all this reorganisation took place at the same time as new legislation was coming into force to improve provision for disabled people – the Chronically Sick and Disabled Persons Act, also passed in 1970. Similar developments occurred a little earlier for Scotland and later for Northern Ireland.

In the early 1970s, new resources were being made available to local authority social services departments and the budget was set to increase by 10 per cent per year. The home help service was expanding and community work initiatives were also giving some staff a new kind of familiarity with local people and the local environment.

Between 1973 and 1977, however, both the UK economy and the political scene experienced a number of serious upheavals and crises. These included soaring inflation and government debt. As a result, the funding passed on to local authorities had to be cut back drastically and, by the mid-1970s, plans to increase budgets for social services had to be revised in many local authorities. Community work and community workers were the first targets for cuts, but as financial pressures increased, serious questions started to be asked about the efficiency of the new social services departments.

4.4 The rise of child protection

As a consequence of the budgetary restrictions, Seebohm's central aim of turning social services into a unified 'fifth service' of the welfare state was never realised. By the end of the 1970s and into the 1980s, a different agenda began to dominate the work of local authority social services departments – work with children. As Roy Parker explains:

> … the issue of child protection was bound to become more prominent. The death of Maria Colwell, who was killed by her stepfather after having been returned home from care, sounded an unmistakable warning (DHSS 1974). The public inquiry that followed was the first of its kind for 30 years; but now it was followed by a veritable plethora of similar inquiries investigating child tragedies.
>
> (Parker, 1995, p. 178)

Social services departments and social workers remained in the firing line of public criticism (Aldridge, 1994). Faced with this, some suggested that the generic approach adopted after Seebohm seemed misguided, when what had always been needed were social workers with specialist knowledge and training in child protection and welfare. Arguably, the kind of generic approach that Seebohm had recommended (which allowed for and encouraged some specialisation once the generic training had been completed) had never been given a chance to develop. But whatever the merits of this argument, social work moved back towards specialisation. Specialist teams were created – working with children, in mental health, with older people, with disabled people, and so on. Of these, child protection work usually came to be regarded as the key specialism in social work and social services departments. The majority of *spending* by local councils was always on care services for older people, but childcare often took priority in terms of the attention given to it by managers and social workers. This was a rather negative development for social care as most service users fall under the 'mental health', 'older people' and 'disability' headings.

However, the governments of the day were aware that much still needed to be done to improve care services for these groups and the 1970s saw a series of government White Papers (draft legislation) that addressed the problems of poor-quality services for the 'mentally handicapped', the 'mentally ill' and older people.

As already mentioned in the previous section, a major NHS reorganisation was carried out in 1974. A further significant shake-up in the health service followed in 1982. Throughout all this, there were repeated calls for greater efficiency and for more joint working between health and social services. The scene was set for the profound restructuring of both social care and health care, and we will look at this next.

Key points

- Social care developed in a fragmented way, divided between the NHS and local authorities. Much of it was still tainted by the Poor Law.
- Care services provided to people's homes and in the community also developed in a patchy way. By the mid-1960s, the dominance of large-scale institutions began to be questioned.
- Social care work never became a universal service in the way health did, despite a major reorganisation of social services in England and Wales following the Seebohm Report and the hope that it would become the 'fifth social service'.
- Social services departments found that they were increasingly preoccupied by 'fire-fighting' crises and high-profile care scandals, especially in childcare.

5 Back to the drawing board?

By the time that a Conservative government came to power with Margaret Thatcher as Prime Minister in 1979, a great deal had changed. The confident years of rebuilding the economy that had followed the Second World War had been replaced by a very different scene. In the 1970s, there had been severe economic crises under both Conservative and Labour governments, inflation had risen to unprecedented levels in the mid-1970s and Britain was falling behind other countries in measures of productivity and growth.

Alongside a difficult economic situation and labour unrest there were increasing demands on the public purse. The numbers of people over retirement age and drawing their state pensions grew rapidly in the 1960s and 1970s. The number of those aged eighty-five or more grew especially fast – with an increase of 40 per cent in the 1960s and of 25 per cent in the 1970s, compared with the previous decades (Victor, 1987). Also, it had been assumed in the 1940s that the NHS would clear a backlog of illness and settle down to a lower level of provision. In practice, the reverse had happened. As the range of treatments expanded and the numbers of older people rose, demands for health care seemed forever to be rising.

As mentioned in the last section, in the mid-1970s the Labour government was forced to implement sharp reductions in public expenditure. In 1977, these amounted to the steepest fall ever seen in a single year, including any of the years in which Margaret Thatcher was Prime Minister in the 1980s. Therefore in terms of setting cash limits on welfare spending, the Labour government of 1974–79 had begun to clear a path for the three administrations of Mrs Thatcher in the 1980s.

For the first time since 1945, the whole welfare state enterprise seemed to be in serious trouble. Questions were being raised about whether it could be afforded. Was it time to go back to the drawing board, 'roll back the state' and begin to dismantle the public sector of health and social care services?

5.1 Understanding 'Thatcherism' and the New Right

The 'Thatcher years' (1979–90) are often portrayed as a period in which decisive government policies fundamentally changed not only the welfare state but also the economy and the political scene.

One of the main explanations for this marked change in government thinking was the growing influence of what have been called *New Right* ideas. At the time, Vic George and Paul Wilding (1985) described these ideas as 'anti-collectivist', which effectively means 'against state intervention'. It is an ideology that favours the private market over public services as the way to meet needs. But what does this mean in practice? One example outside health and social care with which you might be familiar is the 'Right to Buy' policy that was rapidly developed in the early 1980s by the Thatcher government. This gave council tenants incentives (and the right) to buy the house or flat they had been renting from the council. Large numbers of tenants took up the option of buying their own home. They entered the housing market, and by doing this they were actors in a huge transfer of housing from the public sector to the private – a state of affairs that New Right thinking saw as far preferable to state-provided (i.e. local authority) housing. You may recall Lynsey Hanley's account (in Chapter 10 of the Reader) of the impact of this policy for those who remained council tenants, which you read while studying Block 3.

Margaret Thatcher

Margaret Thatcher was elected as leader of the Conservative Party in 1975. Four years later she led the Conservatives to victory over Labour in a general election. She then headed the Conservative governments from 1979 to 1990. Like Tony Blair in 2007, Margaret Thatcher resigned as Prime Minister but was never voted out of office – she was eventually forced to resign by a revolt among fellow Conservatives in Parliament who were worried about losing the next general election.

Next to Winston Churchill, Margaret Thatcher was the most famous and internationally well-known Prime Minister of the UK in the post-war period. She is the only woman to have been Prime Minister. But just a year after winning the 1979 election, Margaret Thatcher had become the most *un*popular Prime Minister since polling began – only to become one of the most popular leaders ever, following success in the Falklands War in 1982. She certainly excited strong opinions: people tended either to love or to loathe her and what she stood for.

Margaret Thatcher cultivated the image of being a 'conviction politician' – that is, a leader who has a clear, firm and non-negotiable set of beliefs and values. In other words, she was the 'Iron Lady', a leader with a mission. She wanted to transform British society and shake up what she saw as its outdated social institutions – the trade unions, the civil service and government, the nationalised industries. Her background helps to explain this: she came from a lower-middle-class family that valued enterprise, individualism and 'bettering yourself' (she was a grocer's daughter – her father was a shopkeeper in Grantham, Lincolnshire). She went to university, where she studied science, and then became a research chemist before marrying a rich and successful businessman, Dennis Thatcher.

In the 1980s, Margaret Thatcher's government set out on a long-term campaign to break trade union power and to sell off state-run industries that were then providing the telephone network and electricity, gas and water supplies. These industries, which had been *collectively* owned, became the property of *individual* shareholders. This reflected her desire above all to develop the free market and to reduce the role of the state. The selling off of council houses to sitting tenants is another example of this. Her successive election victories (1979, 1983 and 1987) seemed to make her invincible, but in the late 1980s she lost a lot of support in the country as a result of imposing a new and highly unpopular form of local taxation, the poll tax. It was this, combined with in-fighting among the Conservative leadership, which led to her downfall.

Why did the New Right or 'anti-collectivist' thinkers urge so strongly that the role of government be drastically reduced? Why did they think it would be much better for public services to be handed over to private sector firms and businesses? As George and Wilding explain:

> Anti-collectivists … see welfare state policies as threatening or damaging to central social values and institutions – the family, work incentives,

> economic development, individual freedom, for example – and in general they are opposed to provision that is more than minimal.
>
> (George and Wilding, 1985, p. 35)

These points are amplified and explained further in Chapter 29 of the Reader, 'The anti-collectivists' by Vic George and Paul Wilding (pages 249–55). And as a summary, the more important criticisms of the welfare state that were put forward by the New Right can be seen in the box below.

The New Right critique of the welfare state

According to New Right thinkers, public services:

- *Drain away a sense of responsibility* and the incentive for people to look after themselves, their families and others in their community. If the state will do it, why bother?
- Tend to develop into a *monopoly* of services. Where there is no competition, the bureaucracies providing health, social care and other services become complacent and inefficient. They can safely afford not to listen to service users.
- Take away *individual freedom* and *choice*. If people cannot buy services in a market, they will have to be 'grateful for what's given' and will have no consumer power through choice between competing providers or sellers.
- Tend to be managed and designed by *welfare professionals, bureaucrats and experts who think they know what's best for the service user*. State services often seem to be clumsy and inappropriate to people's real needs.
- Develop an *insatiable public demand* because they are provided free or on a subsidised basis. If a service is free (as with the NHS), using it incurs very little cost to the individual, so people will tend to use it whether or not they really need it. This in turn leads to lengthy queues or other forms of rationing, and to spiralling costs that can be met only through higher and higher taxation.

The impact of the New Right's pro-market ideas can still be observed in today's health and social care services and the way in which they are organised. In the next activity we will go right back to the beginning of the course to reflect on this point.

Activity 11 The caring business: a legacy of the Thatcher years

Allow about 30 minutes

Turn back to Block 1 of the course and find Section 4 of Unit 3 ('This caring business'). Reread that section and also just the *first page* (p. 146) of Section 5 ('Providing home care: an alternative model'). Now go back over the pages on the New Right in this unit and write a brief answer to each of the following questions:

(a) A key aim of the New Right was to drastically reduce the role of government in paying for and controlling welfare services. Does the example of

Somebody Cares discussed in Unit 3, Section 4 demonstrate that this aim was achieved? Look on the first page (p. 141) for references to official or government bodies – who pays for the services Somebody Cares provides and who checks that these services are up to standard?

(b) New Right thinkers were convinced that the introduction of a care market, with choice and competition between rival providers, would improve the quality of care services because the bad would be driven out of business by the good. After rereading the discussion about Somebody Cares, do you think there is evidence that this has happened? Look out in Section 4 of Unit 3 for references to other care providers in the sector. What do they suggest about the quality of care since the introduction of a care market? Look too at users' views on the first page of Section 5 (p. 146).

(c) Making a profit is a demand on the budget of every private sector care business, including Somebody Cares. Is there any evidence in Section 4 of Unit 3 that this affects the quality or amount of care being provided to the care service user?

Comment

(a) Perhaps you noted the following. First, much of the service provided by Somebody Cares is commissioned by the local authority, in this case Cardiff Social Services, which is central in terms of paying for the services provided to individual clients as well as setting up contracts. Second, in the 'Facts and figures about Somebody Cares' box, there is reference to what is now known as the Care and Social Services Inspectorate for Wales, which is responsible for inspecting care services such as those provided by Somebody Cares. Third, there is reference to the Care Council (for Wales), which regulates the social care workforce, ensuring workers are trained to a certain standard. Equivalent bodies to these exist in each part of the UK. All this suggests that the care market that was set up following the Thatcher period of the 1980s was far from being the kind of free market envisaged by the New Right. Rather than minimal intervention by the state, the hand of government is very evident in today's 'care business'.

(b) Somebody Cares is evidently providing good quality care. As mentioned, inspections had revealed that its standards were exemplary. The staff spoke very positively about the training opportunities they had been given, as well other positive aspects of the way their work was managed. Kevin Madden, who is quoted on page 143 of Unit 3, describes Somebody Cares as a 'good company' and compares it very favourably to some of the others. This suggests that Somebody Cares has not driven out poorer quality rivals. It may be, therefore, that Somebody Cares provides a good service not *because* it exists in a care market but *despite* being in a care market. Indeed, users' criticisms of home care services generally, as listed on the first page of Section 5 in Unit 3 (p. 146), suggest that Somebody Cares may not be typical. These criticisms suggest that the supposed advantages of a market in care, such as greater flexibility and sensitivity to users' needs, less bureaucracy and more choice, are often far from having been fully realised.

(c) As Section 4 of Unit 3 reminds us in the first paragraph, Somebody Cares is a business, 'there to make money as well as provide a service', so as well as staff costs and other overheads, Julie Borek must ensure that a sufficient amount of money is being set aside for profits. When you heard

Julie using such phrases as 'cost constraints' and 'remaining within budget' in Activity 11 of Unit 3, it's worth remembering that they are phrases which partly disguise this profit factor. According to New Right thinkers, the opportunity to make money gives incentives for businesses and entrepreneurs to enter the field and to develop new and better care services. The negative side of the equation, of course, is that profit making means that charges for home care must be high enough to guarantee a profit margin. Where the service user has to contribute to care costs, as in England, this might mean that the service user would really like or actually need more care, but can't afford the additional charges.

While the New Right's criticisms of the welfare state and their suggestions for change towards a more market-driven system had a long-lasting impact, as you have seen in relation to a care business today, the New Right approach was not adopted lock, stock and barrel by the Thatcher administrations of the 1980s.

Margaret Thatcher's government was influenced by the New Right, but it was also pragmatic and cautious in its approach. One reason for this was that she was well aware of the continuing popularity of, and public support for, the welfare state. The introduction of drastic changes in social policy might lose her an election. Thus, there was never any serious possibility that the NHS would be broken up and sold off to health insurance companies in the way that a full-blown free market, New Right approach would have suggested. However, by the mid-1980s the wheels had certainly been set in motion to accomplish large-scale changes in the public sector services.

5.2 Changes in public sector services

Through the Housing Act 1985 and Social Security Act 1986 some significant changes to Beveridge's welfare state were introduced. For instance, reforms in housing limited tenants' rights and reduced the value of housing benefit. Changes to the welfare benefits system meant that people in urgent need could no longer get grants, only loans which had to be repaid. The Social Security Act also cancelled earnings-related unemployment benefit.

As far as the NHS was concerned, Sir Roy Griffiths, a senior director of the Sainsbury's supermarket chain, was asked to conduct an inquiry into its management structures (Griffiths, 1983). As a result, general managers were appointed in hospitals, in an attempt to improve performance and efficiency and curtail the power of the medical profession to determine priorities. In addition, domestic and other support services were being put to the test of the marketplace through competitive tendering. People started to find that the menu in the hospital canteen bore the logo of the firm that had won the contract to do the catering, rather than the name of the hospital, that the porters were wearing private agency uniforms, that the laundry service was the responsibility of a private firm, and that the hospital cleaners were employed by a firm that saw the hospital as so many square metres of floor space to clean at a competitive price. These workers were no longer employed under NHS pay and conditions and the impact of this change was still being felt twenty years on, as the following quotation from a cleaner at Birmingham Heartlands Hospital shows:

> They [the company] don't give the ward cleaning staff any proper facilities, either. If you look just back down the corridor there, you can see a group of cleaning staff sat on chairs in the middle of a public area,

> in their uniforms, taking their break and eating their sandwiches. Some of them carry cups of tea or coffee from their wards down the corridor to come and sit there. You can see them there every day around 10 am.
>
> [...]
>
> It's not just break times: ancillary staff have no shower facilities, and many domestics are forced to get changed in toilets or cupboards on the wards, or to go to and from the hospital in their uniform. That can't be right either. It's not nice for them, and it is a potential hazard.
>
> (Quoted in Unison, 2005, pp. 25–6)

If you are interested, you can read about the effect contracting out has had on the work of porters at the Royal Kensington and Chelsea Hospital, in Chapter 4 of the Reader, 'Portering', by Polly Toynbee (pages 27–36).

Not long after the shake-up of the NHS had begun, Sir Roy Griffiths was also brought in to review social care provision. His report (Griffiths, 1988) was perhaps the most significant sign of change towards a market system for delivering social services. He recommended a clear separation of roles between purchasing and providing agencies in the provision of community care. Local authorities would arrange and commission services but not be the major providers. Rather, there would be a plurality of care providers, including not only local-authority-owned services but also those provided by voluntary organisations and private companies (such as Somebody Cares) from which services could be commissioned. Importantly, however, Griffiths still recommended that local authorities should remain in overall control of social service provision.

The influence of the 1988 Griffiths Report was clearly apparent in a government White Paper, *Caring for People: Community Care in the Next Decade and Beyond* (DH, 1989a). This, together with a health White Paper, *Working for Patients* (DH, 1989b), prepared the way for the NHS and Community Care Act 1990 for England, Wales and Scotland. Similar legislation was passed a year later in Northern Ireland.

As well as introducing a split between purchase and provision in social care services, the 1990 Act also introduced a split between planning and provision in the NHS in England and Wales. Now health authorities and social services departments in England and Wales were to become purchasers – that is, they were to assess needs within their areas and arrange to meet them by issuing contracts to others.

How did these changes affect those who were working in health and social care? One former social worker recalls:

> In the run up to the Act, I felt positive about it because I had read that it would give service users more choice. We were told we had to assess people's needs and also take their wishes into account. Actually I didn't think this would be new, but it seemed like a good idea to make it a requirement.
>
> Once the Act came in, the main difference was the amount of forms which had to be filled in before any kind of service could be applied for. We had to get separate assessment forms filled out by everyone. The whole process seemed to take much longer than before. I found it quite embarrassing to visit a new family and spend several visits asking them about everything on the form without being able to hold out any hope of a service! You couldn't start looking for a service until you got the go-ahead from the assessment panel.
>
> (Personal communication)

Health care goes to market

What this quotation illustrates is that the role of social workers was undergoing a major change. They were no longer to be providers of care and support. Rather, they were to become assessors, deciding whether or not the local authority should arrange and financially support those who requested help. This was a very different vision of social work from the universal service envisaged by Seebohm twenty years earlier.

At the time, there were both supporters and critics of these reforms, which had been inspired by the New Right.

The *supporters* argued that change was long overdue. It was good to shake up the complacency of the institutions of the old-style Beveridgean welfare state, which had neglected to consider outcomes and costs and to pay attention to economy, efficiency and effectiveness. The new arrangements freed up thinking and promised real innovation, choice and flexibility for users. The transformation of clients into customers was a form of empowerment – putting service users in the driving seat.

The *critics* argued that the main problem of both health and social care services was that they were under-resourced. Money that could have been used for care would be poured into setting up new systems and into private profit. Caring work would be pushed back on to the shoulders of unpaid carers. Employers of low-paid staff in the private and voluntary sectors would inevitably try to undercut each other to gain contracts and so would reduce workers' pay even further. Real market relationships would not be possible and to think about people in need of care as 'customers' who could exercise choice was inappropriate.

So who was right? Whatever the answer to this question might be, one thing is certain: the change of direction that was heralded in during the 1980s set the agenda for the newly elected Labour government in 1997. This is something you will find out more about in the next unit.

Key points

- The welfare state arrived at an important crossroads in the late 1970s. Because of economic problems and rising demand for welfare services, the view that the 'Beveridgean' welfare state needed a major overhaul gained ground.
- A Conservative government, elected in 1979 and led by Margaret Thatcher, was influenced by New Right ideas that suggested that the welfare state was counter-productive.
- The Conservative government of the late 1980s and early 1990s transformed arrangements for the delivery of health and social care by introducing the idea of markets, purchasers and providers.
- The changes introduced by the Conservatives took several years to take effect, but as they did, they set the agenda for an incoming Labour government in 1997.

Conclusion

At the start of this unit we suggested that you put together your own list or 'timeline' of significant milestones in the development of health and social care. Now, in this last activity, we'd like you to complete your timeline.

Activity 12 Milestones in health, social care and your own family

Allow about one hour

(a) First, review the 'Milestones in UK health and social care' column of your timeline. Do you feel that you have included all the key items? Do you need to check back over parts of the unit to fill in missing items? Does reading through the milestones help to give you an overall picture of developments in health and social care policy since 1940? Do you need to add a few notes to summarise key changes?

(b) Second, review the 'Personal milestones' column of your timeline. Pick a significant milestone and remind yourself what was happening in health and social care at the time. Write a note or two about whether you or your family were affected by what was going on. Then do the same for another one or two significant personal milestones. Has doing this revealed interesting connections between your own life and the changing shape of health and social care services? This is something you could discuss with other students in the online forums.

(c) Third, visit the course website, and click on the link to the HSC Resource Bank. Click on Milestones. Then search for, say, five key items from your own timeline, such as the Race Relations Act 1976 or the National Health Service and Community Care Act 1990. As you find each one, click on it to see what additional information you are given. Are there any useful points to add to your own timeline? When you have explored the HSC Resource Bank milestones as much as you want to, log off.

DVD

(d) Finally, review your timeline and consider whether it is worth producing a typed version. If you think it is, go back to Unit 21 Activity 1 on the DVD, reopen the Activity Notes, type in the notes you have made and print it off.

Comment

It can be very interesting to compare what was happening on the broader stage of the welfare state with what was happening in your own personal history or that of your family. For instance, Ken (the first author of this unit) was born on the very day that the NHS launched into action on 5 July 1948. To his parents' relief this meant that free midwifery, district nursing and doctor's services had just become available (Blakemore, 2005). You might not be able to find such a close connection between the development of care services and your own personal history, but at the very least it might be illuminating to be able to 'pin' the milestones in health and social care to key events in your life or in the history of your own family. Doing this should make the landmarks and key dates in the history of health and social care more memorable and relevant. Even if you or your parents were not born in the UK, you will be able to think about what was happening in their world or in your surroundings then, and compare this with what was happening in the UK at the same time.

One purpose of this activity was simply to explore the HSC Resource Bank in order to see how much useful information is available to you there. If you are going on to take other Health and Social Care courses, this is a resource that will always be available to you if you want to cross-check something you are reading, or if you need information for an essay.

In the activity you have just completed, you have been looking back over the broad sweep of changes that led to the creation of a welfare state and to the subsequent development of health and social care. Now that we have reached the end of the unit, let's check back over the three core questions posed at the beginning.

- What are the underlying principles and ideas on which the UK welfare state is based?

Following the Second World War, an overwhelming majority of people wanted to live in a society that was more equal and fair than pre-war Britain had been. People wanted public services free at the point of use and the same services and benefits for everyone. So the two principles *equality* and *fairness*, combined with a third, *universalism*, formed the bedrock of the welfare state. But don't forget that another rather different principle was built into the 'Beveridgean' welfare state – the *insurance* principle. This was meant to make the means test a thing of the past, although quite soon after 1946 it was beginning to fail to do this.

We went on to see how the story of the welfare state in the last quarter of the twentieth century was basically one of how the *market* principle gradually became more important.

- What major changes in direction have occurred in government's approach to the welfare state since it was introduced?

The most significant change in direction to have taken place in government's approach to the welfare state in the last century was the shift from a 'one-size-fits-all' kind of welfare state (with uniform services directed from the centre) to one where there is market-like competition between all the various parts. In some areas the state was replaced by the private sector and private firms, in others it wasn't – as in the NHS – but even here, market-like competition was developed (although much less so in Wales and Northern Ireland and not in Scotland) and various services, such as laundry and cleaning, were privatised. The NHS remained the most enduring example of the traditional, all-inclusive welfare principle and was still a popular institution after five decades of organisational change and crisis.

- What did the twentieth-century welfare state achieve for health and social care?

As you've probably guessed, it's impossible to put the welfare state as a whole on the weighing scales to find out whether it was either a success or a failure in the ways in which it delivered health and social care.

Let's take the health service first. On the one hand, the NHS not only proved itself to be popular, accessible and widely used, but also delivered comprehensive health care economically, compared to the cost of running health services in comparable industrial countries. On the other hand, outcomes have often seemed disappointing because people's expectations of their own health, and what the health service can do to help them, have risen faster than actual improvements in NHS performance. Also, rather than mopping up a pool of illness and reducing sickness rates, as the architects of the NHS had hoped, Britain's free health service struggled to cope all through the twentieth century with steadily rising demand. Survival rates improved, mainly as a result of better living and working conditions in Britain's post-war welfare state. But this meant that increasing numbers of people were living longer to 'enjoy' the diseases of old age, thus putting more demands on the NHS.

The social care system developed more slowly than health services and in many ways remained the 'poor relation' of health care. But with limited resources and services that were often stretched to capacity, there was a great deal of improvement in both the range and volume of social services available. Much depends on the standpoint we take when we're assessing progress in social care made in the last century. As we saw, provision never caught up with demand for social care services. The various reorganisations of local authority social services left a lot to be desired in terms of providing an effective and responsive service, and successive governments failed to integrate the systems providing health and social care. From the standpoint of the 1940s, though, social and residential care had been transformed by the end of the twentieth century. Patchy and unfair though the system still was, it could nevertheless record some marked achievements – the closure of many large, grim, residential institutions; the introduction of at least a semblance of choice in some services; and a more honest and open recognition of the problems that were all too often hidden from view in the 1940s, such as child abuse, elder abuse and problems of mental ill health and disability.

Learning skills: Coping with exam anxiety

However 'rational' you manage to be about the exam, you are likely to experience some anxiety. Exams put you under pressure, as you read in Section 12.1 of Chapter 12 of *The Good Study Guide* (when you were working on Unit 16), and this pressure has both good and bad effects. Stress supplies the energy and motivation to push you to peak performances and bring out your true ability. But if it isn't controlled and channelled, it can also lead to a build-up of anxiety, to a point where it begins to have bad effects both on your exam performance and on you.

DVD

Activity 13 Managing anxiety

Allow about 20 minutes

It's important to be aware of the common effects of anxiety, so that you can recognise them and work out ways of overcoming them. If you go to Block 6, Unit 21, Activity 13 on the DVD you will find a quiz that will help you to do this.

Comment

Most of us feel anxious before exams. So it is important to:

- be aware of effects that anxiety can have on you as you prepare for and take the exam
- work out ways of overcoming anxiety.

Anxiety can have a variety of effects, which people cope with in different ways. But, in essence, it comes down to:

- facing up to thinking ahead to the exam
- getting clear in your mind *what* you need to do and *how* you will go about it

- talking to *other people*
- getting working (instead of worrying).

Don't let anxiety get you down. Remember this is *your* course. You paid for it. And it's your exam. Get what *you* need from it. Don't let it get the upper hand. Use the tension to get the best out of yourself.

End-of-unit checklist

Having studied this unit you should be able to:

- understand the principle of universalism on which the welfare state was based
- describe the main features of the key social reforms that created the welfare state in the 1940s
- show a broad understanding of how health and social care services developed and how they were organised in the post-war period of the welfare state
- reflect on what the welfare state in general, and health and social care in particular, had achieved by the end of the twentieth century.

References

Aldridge, M. (1994) *Making Social Work News*, London, Routledge.

Beveridge, J. (1954) *Beveridge and his Plan*, London, Hodder and Stoughton.

Beveridge, W. (1942) *Social Insurance and Allied Services* (The Beveridge Report), Cmd 6404, London, HMSO.

Blakemore, K. (1998) *Social Policy: An Introduction*, Buckingham, Open University Press.

Blakemore, K. (2005) *Sunnyside Down: Growing Up in '50s Britain*, Stroud, Sutton Publishing.

Dale, J. and Foster, P. (1986) *Feminists and State Welfare*, London, Routledge.

Department of Health (DH) (1989a) *Caring for People: Community Care in the Next Decade and Beyond*, London, HMSO.

Department of Health (DH) (1989b) *Working for Patients*, London, HMSO.

Department of Health and Social Security (DHSS) (1974) *Report of the Committee of Inquiry into the Care and Supervision provided in relation to Maria Colwell*, London, HMSO.

Esmail, A. (2007) 'Asian doctors in the NHS: service and betrayal', *British Journal of General Practice*, vol. 57, no. 534, pp. 827–34.

Esmail, A., Abel, P. and Everington, S. (2003) 'Discrimination in the discretionary points awards scheme: comparison of white and non-white consultants and men with women', *British Medical Journal*, vol. 326, no. 7391, pp. 687–8.

Esmail, A., Everington, S. and Doyle, H. (1998) 'Racial discrimination in the allocation of distinction awards? Analysis of list of award holders by type of award, specialty and region', *British Medical Journal*, vol. 316, no. 7126, pp. 193–5.

Field, D. (2003) 'Health care in contemporary Britain' in Taylor, S. and Field, D. (eds) *Sociology of Health and Health Care*, Oxford, Blackwell.

Fraser, D. (1984) *The Evolution of the British Welfare State* (2nd edn), Basingstoke, Macmillan.

George, V. and Wilding, P. (1985) *Ideology and Social Welfare*, London, Routledge & Kegan Paul.

Goffman, E. (1961) *Asylums: Essays on the Social Situation of Mental Patients and Other Inmates*, New York, Doubleday.

Griffiths, R. (1983) *NHS Management Inquiry Report*, London, Department of Health and Social Security.

Griffiths, R. (1988) *Community Care: Agenda for Action*, London, HMSO.

Hallett, C. (1995) *Women and Social Policy: An Introduction*, Hemel Hempstead, Prentice Hall.

Hasluck, C. (2000) 'Early lessons from the evaluation of New Deal programmes', *Labour Market Trends*, vol. 108, no. 8, pp. 353–80.

Hennessy, P. (1992) *Never Again: Britain 1945–51*, London, Vintage.

Hetherington, P. (2000) 'Jobless forced to take lessons', *Guardian*, 12 January [online], www.guardian.co.uk/money/2000/jan/12/workandcareers.uknews (Accessed 29 November 2008).

Klein, R. (1989) *The Politics of the National Health Service* (2nd edn), London, Croom Helm.

Lewis, J. (1983) *Women's Welfare, Women's Rights*, London, Croom Helm.

Mares, P., Henley, A. and Baxter, C. (1985) *Health Care in Multiracial Britain*, Cambridge, Health Education Council/National Extension College.

McNaught, A. (1988) *Race and Health Policy*, Beckenham, Croom Helm.

Means, R. and Smith, R. (1994) *Community Care: Policy and Practice*, Basingstoke, Macmillan.

Oral History of Geriatrics as a Speciality, Dr Samuel Vine interviewed by Anthea Holme (1991), British Library Sound Archive C512/68/01-02 [tape 1 side A]; http://cadensa/bl/uk (Accessed 2 November 2008).

Owen, D. (2003) 'The demographic characteristics of people from minority ethnic groups in Britain' in Mason, D. (ed.) *Explaining Ethnic Differences*, Bristol, The Policy Press.

Parker, R. (1995) 'Child care and the personal social services' in Gladstone, D. (ed.) *British Social Welfare*, London, UCL Press.

Seebohm, F. (1968) *Report of the Committee on Local Authority and Allied Personal Social Services*, Cmnd 3703, London, HMSO.

Smith, D.J. (1980) *Overseas Doctors in the National Health Service*, London, Policy Studies Institute.

Stevenson, J. and Cook, C. (1994) *Britain in the Depression: Society and Politics 1920–39* (2nd edn), Harlow, Longman.

Taylor, D.I. and Esmail, A. (1999) 'Retrospective analysis of census data on general practitioners who qualified in South Asia: who will replace them as they retire?', *British Medical Journal*, vol. 318, no. 7179, pp. 306–10.

Taylor, S. and Field, D. (eds) (2003) *Sociology of Health and Health Care* (3rd edn), Oxford, Blackwell.

Thane, P. (1982) *The Foundations of the Welfare State*, London, Longman.

Townsend, P. (1962) *The Last Refuge: A Survey of Residential Institutions and Homes of Old People*, London, Routledge & Kegan Paul.

Unison (2005) *Cleaners' Voices: Interviews with Hospital Cleaning Staff* [online], www.unison.org.uk/acrobat/14565.pdf (Accessed 15 February 2008).

Victor, C. (1987) *Old Age in Modern Society*, London, Chapman & Hall.

Unit 22

What future for health and social care?

Prepared for the course team by Ken Blakemore and Julia Johnson

Contents

Introduction

In Unit 21 we looked back at the last century and at how health and social care had developed up to the end of the 1990s. In this unit we will be looking forwards to the social landscape ahead of us in the twenty-first century, reflecting on both the current scene and the prospects for health and social care.

Working out *exactly* what lies on the road ahead isn't possible, of course. But it is possible to identify the key issues and challenges that have been picked out as the most likely to affect health and social care in profound ways. Most of these have already been mentioned in previous units of this course. They include such issues as the ageing of society, growing ethnic and racial diversity, changing family structures and the impact of poverty and low income on people providing care and on those receiving it. In the first three sections of this unit, we will take stock of these trends and what they mean for health and social care. In Sections 4 and 5 we will be looking at some key issues in care policy and at some of the challenges and pressures facing health and social care in the twenty-first century. In particular, we will be considering how ways of meeting the demands relating to choice and control in an increasingly diverse society are being tackled.

Core questions

- What kind of society is emerging in the UK of the twenty-first century and how are key features of this society affecting health and social care?
- What have been the main developments in health and social care policy since 2000?
- What are the key issues and challenges facing health and social care in the twenty-first century?

Are you taking the IVR?

If you are studying K101 as part of the Integrated Vocational Route (IVR), don't forget to check your VQ Candidate Handbook to see which Unit 22 activities contribute to your electronic portfolio.

1 The social context of care

The end of the twentieth century was a significant milestone for the welfare state and therefore for health and social care, but what are the grounds for suggesting this? The most obvious landmark was a political one – the election of New Labour to government in 1997. Despite their landslide election victory and talk of bold new approaches to tackle Britain's problems, however, Labour's plans for health and social services were a mix of the previous Conservative government's policies and some new policies of their own (Powell, 1999). They certainly didn't represent anything like the scale of reform or the break with the past undertaken by the Labour government that introduced the welfare state between 1945 and 1951.

British Prime Minister Tony Blair, celebrating the Labour Party's landslide victory in 1997 with his wife, Cherie Blair

The end of the century was also a landmark for other, more general reasons. Five decades had passed since the introduction of the universal system of state welfare. Many 'baby boomers', the generation born just after the Second World War, were becoming grandparents. And two generations had been born since the arrival in the 1950s and 1960s of substantial numbers of black and Asian people from the Caribbean, the Indian subcontinent and other areas of the world. Therefore by the late 1990s it was possible to observe the long-term impact of the welfare state on British society. How much had the UK gained by being one of the first welfare states, and did it look as though the benefits had been shared fairly?

1.1 'Patchwork Britain'

To answer this question we can make a start by looking at a general overview of British society at the end of the last century. David Coates, a political scientist, has provided such an overview, using the telling phrase 'patchwork Britain' (Coates, 2005, p. 20) to summarise the diversity and new social divisions that had become evident since the 1940s.

Reader

Activity 1 Looking at Britain's social landscape

Allow about 50 minutes

Read Chapter 30, 'The slow birth of New Labour Britain', by David Coates in the Reader (pages 257–63). As you do so, think about how the points the author makes might be relevant to health and/or social care in some way. Look particularly for his comments on:

- the decline in what he calls a '*sense of solidarity*' in the UK since the 1940s
- the steady rise in the percentage of *women in paid work*
- the fact that the UK has become a *more unequal society* since the 1970s.

When you've finished reading the chapter:

(a) In a column on the left-hand side of a sheet of paper, list the three points mentioned above. Now in a separate column on the right-hand side, write a brief comment next to each point on *why* you think it might have significant implications for health and/or social care.

(b) What other points raised by David Coates struck you as possibly being relevant to health and social care? Select *one* further point. Add it to your list and write a brief comment on why you think it's significant.

Comment

David Coates has raised a lot of points about the ways in which the UK has changed since the 1940s. But first, let's look at the three points listed above. You might like to compare your own notes with the comments in the grid below.

There has been a *decline in* what Coates calls a '*sense of solidarity*' in the UK since the 1940s. This has been caused partly by the break-up of and decline in traditional working-class communities and partly by increased social and geographical mobility.	*You will have picked up from your study of Block 1 and Block 3, Unit 10 that the networks of community and family that used to provide a source of social activities, care and a sense of identity and mutual support are not as strong as they were.*
The *rise* in the number of *women in paid work* represents an enormous social change. In the 1950s, the overwhelming majority of women over twenty-one were married and were predominantly in domestic roles. The change has occurred partly because of an underlying trend away from heavy industry and the rapid increase in new jobs in the service sector, many of which have been taken by women working part-time.	*As many women are now in paid work they find it more difficult to take on caring responsibilities at home. Ann Walker, as you may recall, had to give up her job to care for Angus McPhail. Also, in some areas of the country, care homes and social services might experience difficulties in finding staff, because care workers' wages are sometimes lower than those paid in the service sector – for example, to checkout attendants at the local supermarket.*
The UK is a *more unequal society* compared with the situation between the 1940s and 1970s.	*The UK has a majority of people with rising living standards and incomes but, as you found out in Block 3, a significant number of individuals, social groups and whole areas have not had their fair share of these improvements – they have been marginalised. People who are being cared for and those who are full-time informal carers have a higher than average chance of being in the marginalised and low-income groups.*

In the grid that follows you will see some of the additional points that we have picked out, all of which seem relevant to health and social care in some way. Perhaps you managed to pick out one of these points as well. If you had any difficulty, however, don't worry at this stage. As you work through the unit, the knack of looking at health and social care 'in the round' and seeing care in its social context should develop naturally – and you can always revisit this activity when you are revising.

Additional points raised by David Coates's overview	
The UK's *'social fabric'* – its schools, hospitals, social services, social sector housing and transport infrastructure – experienced decades of *under-investment* compared with other European countries.	*Health and social care are vital parts of a wider infrastructure. If that infrastructure has problems, such as expensive housing, congested roads and inadequate public transport, it becomes harder to staff and to run health and social care services – as illustrated, for example, by the nurse who was unable to find affordable housing close to her work.*
The UK is *no longer a society dominated by the state and the public sector* in the ways in which it was in the 1940s.	*It has become 'normal' to expect social care services to be provided by a complicated network of private, voluntary and local authority agencies. As you have seen, much home care is now provided by agencies such as Somebody Cares. And Jordan, whom you read about in Block 2, was found a foster home by Foster Care Associates – a private company set up in 1994. Even the NHS, although still a largely public service, also relies increasingly on the private sector – especially in England – to provide medical treatment and other frontline services, such as cleaning.*
Rates of divorce and separation and the numbers of lone parents have increased dramatically in the UK since the 1950s.	*Family break-ups and changes in relationships and partners can mean that it becomes more difficult for some people to provide care to others. It also means that some people needing intimate personal care are less likely to be able to call on a partner or others close by for help. Angus, as you may remember, was Ann's stepfather, which affected her attitude towards caring for him.*
The UK has a much *bigger middle class* compared with the 1940s. Sociologists have described this as the rise of a 'managerial' middle class.	*By the end of the 1990s, people in the managerial middle class were employed increasingly in the public as well as the private sector – for instance, in hospital management. 'Managerialism' – which means the application of business techniques to running organisations – has become a dominant influence in both health and social care.*
Coates does not use the term '*consumer culture*' but he refers to the development of a society in which the majority of people now expect to own their own cars and houses, to take holidays and possess a wide range of consumer goods. This is in stark contrast to food rationing and other post-war restrictions in the 1940s and early 1950s.	*This has important implications for the world of health and social care. Through widespread use of the internet and mobile phones, many people now inhabit a world of rapid, responsive service. They expect to be able to make choices and to find individual solutions to their problems and needs in ways that did not occur to people before. You may remember, for example, the chapters you have read from the Reader about how people use the internet not only to learn about health issues and treatments, but also to find support through chat rooms and other online forums.*
The UK is now a significantly *more multicultural, racially diverse* country than it used to be. However, problems of racism and ethnic discrimination remain.	*As you learned from Unit 11, ethnic and racial diversity challenges the idea of presenting people with 'one-size-fits-all' services in health and social care. And ethnic diversity raises a more general question about whether 'mainstream' care services should be varied and adapted to the requirements of all minority groups, including, for instance, the different faith communities, or gay and lesbian people – not just minority ethnic communities.*

This poster was produced during the Second World War when many materials were in short supply and people were encouraged to recycle unwanted and worn out items

Consumerism in the twenty-first century has led some to refer to the UK as a 'throwaway' society

You might have noticed that apart from briefly mentioning the phrase 'an ageing population', Coates does not discuss the issue of demographic change – that is, changes to the overall characteristics of a population, such as the proportion of men and women or of people in different age groups – and the challenges this poses. Nor does he have much to say about trends in health and illness in British society. So now that we've looked at the social context in outline, let's focus next (in Section 2) on these two very important trends in the UK. Both the ageing population and trends in health and illness are particularly relevant to the world of care.

Key points

- Health and social care don't take place in a vacuum. Care services are shaped by the changing social context.
- The 'social context' includes family and household structure, culture and ethnic identity, the amount of money people have, attitudes to care services, and many other influences.
- The UK in the twenty-first century has become a more individualised, consumer-oriented, unequal and diverse society than it was in the middle of the last century.
- These trends are challenging the idea of providing uniform health and social care services.

2 Health trends in an ageing society

The significance of the ageing of the UK population has been referred to briefly in various parts of the course. The media often portray the growth in numbers of older people as a 'demographic time bomb' which, when it explodes, will put an intolerable burden on both the health and social care systems and the pensions system. But is this alarmist approach justified?

2.1 The ageing society: a looming problem for care?

When you hear talk of an ageing society, what kind of thoughts come into your mind? Are they negative and pessimistic, mainly positive or somewhere in between? Are you picturing increasingly hard-pressed families and understaffed care services struggling to cope with rapidly rising numbers of frail older people? If you are, you might also have been wondering what the knock-on effects of the ageing society will be. What about the *younger* people needing care – Jordan, for example – if families and care services have to put increasing efforts into caring for older people?

Let's tackle these questions first by looking at some official estimates of how fast the numbers of older people are likely to grow between now and 2021.

Activity 2 The ageing society: keeping a sense of proportion

Allow about 20 minutes

Look at the two graphs in Figures 1 and 2. Once you have taken in both graphs, write down a short answer to each of the following questions:

(a) When you looked at the first graph, what was running through your mind when you saw the line indicating the numbers of people aged 65 and over?

(b) The first graph also includes a line to show the numbers and projected numbers of younger people – 'dependants' under the age of 16. What are the implications for care commitments, do you think, of this line in the graph?

(c) And what were your reactions to the projected increases in the numbers of people aged 90 and over, in the second graph? Did you see these as a cause for concern, or not?

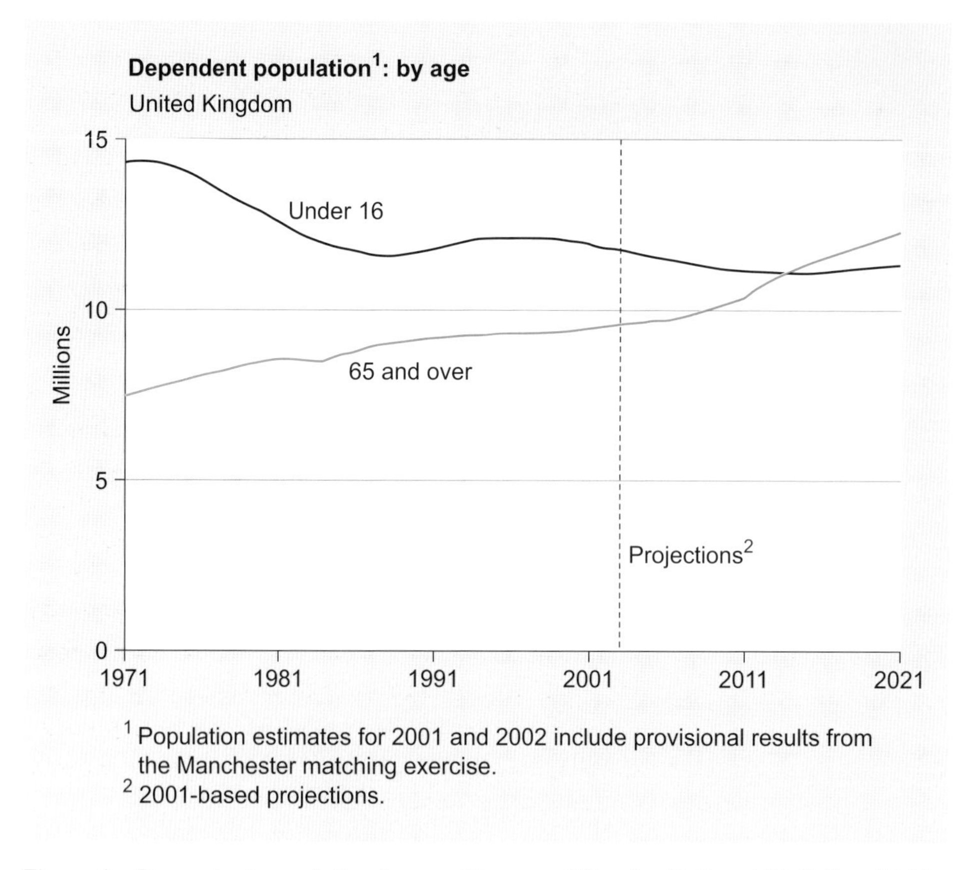

Figure 1 Dependent population by age (Source: Office for National Statistics, 2004, p. 17, Figure 1.3)

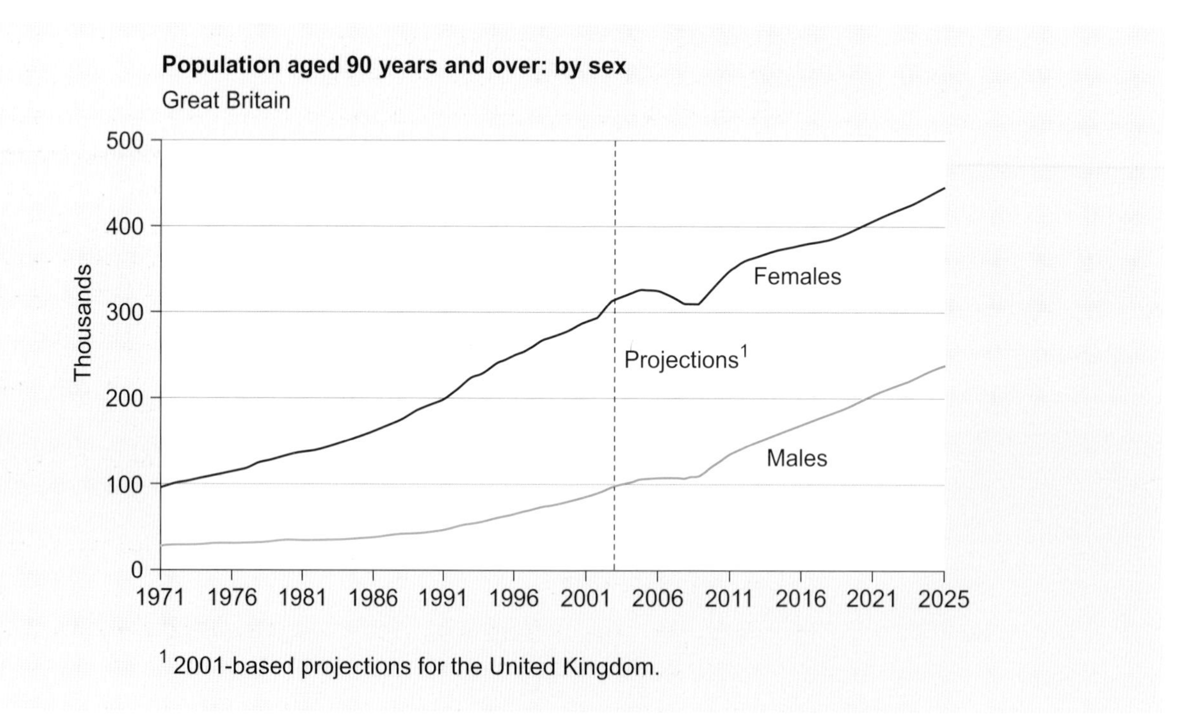

Figure 2 Population aged 90 years and over by sex (Source: Office for National Statistics, 2004, p. 17, Figure 1.4)

Comment

(a) What is striking in the first graph is how *gradual* the increase in the numbers of older people is projected to be up to the year 2021. It's relatively steady – pretty much the same trend as in preceding decades. Nothing about this graph looks like a fever chart with sharp rises and falls, or a worryingly steep climb up to the top right-hand corner. But of course what we make of information like this depends very much on our pre-existing attitudes and concerns. If we don't like the idea of growing numbers of older people in society, we could find ways to see this information as worrying. For instance, another way of looking at this graph could be to say that the numbers of people over the age of 65 will have risen by a third by 2021 (from the total in 1971), from under ten million to about fifteen million. Five million extra is certainly a big increase – an extra million pensioners every decade – and five million is greater than the size of whole populations of some countries, such as Ireland, Norway or Scotland. On the other hand, we might have the attitude that the more people aged over 65 there are in society the better, as this is a sign of success in raising living standards and life expectancy. Also, it's incorrect to assume that older people are unproductive or that they make no contribution to health and social care. In fact, older people are often the main carers of other older people, as well as providing vital childcare services in many families.

(b) The expected decline in numbers of under-16s shown in the graph could be interpreted as both good and bad news for health and social care. Having fewer children will compensate the middle-aged for the likely increase in caring responsibilities towards their ageing parents. This is especially the case in terms of the economic cost. Most under-16s are financially dependent on their families, but most older people are financially independent (more than that, some share in meeting the costs incurred by young members of the family, such as university fees or paying a deposit on their first home purchase). On the other hand, a shrinking younger generation can be bad news if it becomes a long-term trend, as the supply of young people to work in care homes, social services and in nursing will diminish just as the care system comes under strain. Any significant immigration could help to offset this problem, though, as it did in the 1950s and 1960s and was doing in the first decade of the twenty-first century: most migrants are young.

(c) The second graph shows a steeper rise in the numbers of very old people (over 90) compared with those over 65 as a whole. In the UK:

- Many more people are surviving into very old age, compared with the past.
- Between 1971 and 2002 the number of people aged over 90 tripled to more than 380,000.
- By the year 2021 there will be over 600,000 men and women in this 'very old' group.

This worries many who are concerned about the extra costs of caring for growing numbers of very old people. But again, there is a positive as well as a negative angle on this. On the positive side, it's a great achievement – both for the individual and for society. It shows how the long-term improvements in health, education and welfare fostered by the 'Beveridgean' welfare state of the 1940s have paid off. However, much depends on whether the health gains for older people can be sustained in the future and also on what their expectations of health care will be. These are the things, rather than sheer numbers, that will determine what demands they actually place on the care system.

The triumphant centenarian who in April 2007 collected winnings of £25,000 from a bet that he would live to see his 100th birthday. Bookmaker William Hill subsequently changed the stake for new bets to 110 years.

Rather than concentrating on the numbers who are expected to survive to a certain age, it's more helpful to focus on how many healthy life years the average man and woman can expect to live. We will return to this point in Section 2.2 below where we review trends in health and illness.

Another important reason for not getting too fixated on the headline numbers of older people expected in the future is because it's not the totals that matter so much as the *proportion* or percentage of older people in the population. From this point of view, the proportion of people over retirement age is expected to rise between 2001 and 2021 from just under one in five of the UK population to about one in four (Taylor and Field, 2007, p. 114). So, as with the overall total, this rise will be significant but relatively gradual. What it means is that the balance between older and younger people is changing.

In sum, it would be wrong to exaggerate the impact of the ageing society or to see it only as a looming problem. Official estimates of future numbers of older people in the UK indicate a steady but relatively gradual increase, at least until 2021. As Phil Mullan (2000) suggests, these figures certainly do not justify the alarmist approach in much of the media coverage of this topic. And as Sara Arber and Jay Ginn (2006) argue, the so-called 'burden' of the older population on the care system might be less than expected. Let's take this argument further by looking at trends in health and illness to see how these affect the picture.

2.2 Health trends in the UK in the twenty-first century

Starting with the negative and concentrating on problems can sometimes mean that we get stuck in that mindset. This is often the case when we think about the state of people's health in the UK, or about the prospects for people with long-term or chronic illnesses.

Let's see how we might be able to think about things a little differently. You will recall being introduced to Anwar Malik in Unit 2 of Block 1, a fictional person whose story of living with diabetes illustrated some common trends in illness and disability. In the next activity you will be able to reflect on what happened to Anwar. His story is representative of some negative experiences of illness and of care services. But how widespread is this kind of experience? Before you start Activity 3, read about Omar Naseem in the box below.

Omar Naseem

Like Anwar Malik, Omar Naseem is also a fictional person. Let's suppose that he is the same age as Anwar, that he's also a Muslim from Pakistan, and that he has also just been told that he has Type 2 diabetes. However, unlike Anwar, Omar lives not just with his wife, Jasmin, but also with two grown-up sons. Their wives and children also live with Omar and Jasmin. The whole family occupies three small terraced houses that have been knocked together to make one large, shared dwelling. Omar has a third son living in the same city, who has recently qualified as a doctor and is applying to work in a GP practice. Omar's only daughter is a pharmacist.

Omar himself is the prosperous owner of a local computer sales and repair business, although he doesn't work as many hours as he used to because one of his sons is gradually taking over the running of the business.

Activity 3 Rewriting Anwar Malik

Allow about 15 minutes

Spend a few minutes reviewing in your mind what happened to Anwar Malik (in Block 1, Unit 2) during his 'patient career' through primary and secondary care. Remember that he is a fictional person. Now write down:

(a) two key factors in Anwar's personal circumstances and his experiences of health care that you think put him at a disadvantage, resulting in the negative outcomes for him described in Unit 2

(b) two things that you think might have resulted in a more positive health outcome if we had been looking at Omar instead of Anwar.

Comment

(a) We thought the following things put Anwar at a disadvantage:

- The first and perhaps the most obvious was connected to his minority ethnic identity and social status. In short, Anwar experienced some institutional racism. The GP practice had failed to put a system in place to respond sensitively and immediately to the diverse requirements of all its service users. The dietary advice Anwar received, for instance, didn't take account of his religious beliefs and the dietary prohibitions he had to observe as a Muslim.
- Second, Anwar seemed to have rather low expectations of health in later life. He tried to downplay his symptoms and preferred to see them as 'just slowing down with age' rather than as signs of a treatable illness. Later on, he didn't keep to his recommended treatment programme. The health practitioners with whom he came into contact failed to help him either to overcome some of these personal barriers to accepting the nature of his illness, or to understand fully what he had to do to avoid 'complications' and eventually a leg amputation.

(b) It's possible to imagine a different scenario for someone like Omar:

- First, Omar lives in a large three-generation household, which is not uncommon among Pakistani and Bangladeshi communities in the UK. At least one and possibly more sons often live with their father after getting married. This would not *necessarily* have resulted in a better outcome for Omar. Although in practice most Asian families are very supportive of their older or senior members, it would be wrong to assume that all provide caring environments that give unconditional support to older relatives or others needing care (Blakemore and Boneham, 1994; Blakemore, 2000; McKenzie et al., 2008). But Omar's sons and daughters-in-law would at least have been closer at hand, compared with Anwar's situation, and more likely to notice and comment on changes in his health. This would not have prevented the onset of diabetes, of course, but it might have helped Omar to feel more positive than Anwar did about managing and treating the illness, and might well have prevented the kind of deterioration that led in Anwar's case to a leg amputation.

- Second, Omar would be more likely to have higher expectations of his health and quality of life than Anwar did. It's also likely that he would have more knowledge of how to manage diabetes – he would be using the internet straight away – and have higher expectations of doctors and of the health care system. And if he was unclear about what to do about his diabetes problem or how to monitor his blood glucose levels, perhaps his son or daughter would be able to help.

Belonging to a racial, ethnic and religious minority makes it likely that Omar would encounter the same kinds of ethnic and racial discrimination in his dealings with the health services as Anwar did. But by giving Omar a higher social class position we would have a more certain chance of improving his health outcomes. Neither Omar's position as the prosperous owner of a local computer sales business nor the fact that his son has recently qualified as a doctor, or his daughter as a pharmacist, are uncommon in the minority Asian communities of the twenty-first-century UK.

As Tariq Modood et al. (1997) have shown, some sections of some of the UK's minority ethnic communities were already achieving upward social mobility and considerable economic and social success in the 1980s and 1990s. People with more social advantages than Anwar – with higher incomes and more education, as in the case of Omar – are much more likely to have higher expectations of their own health and to demand more from the health care system (Wilkinson, 1996). Of course, changing 'Anwar' to 'Omar' wouldn't guarantee better health outcomes, but the point is that it would be likely to do so. Positive outcomes occur in the same way as negative ones do.

'Rewriting Anwar Malik' might help you to see that, although Anwar was a very useful example for illustrating health care issues in Block 1, focusing on the sorts of problems he encountered could give you a rather distorted picture of trends in health and illness. First, Anwar's case might have given you the impression that a lot of Asian and black people experience more health problems than do people in the majority white community. The relationship between ethnicity and health is a complex one, but careful studies of patterns of illness in minority communities have shown that most of what *appear* to be 'ethnic' differences can be accounted for by social class and income differences (Modood et al., 1997; Health Education Authority, 2000; Nazroo, 2001). In other words, patterns in the health of middle-class Asian and black people are, by and large, similar to patterns in the health of middle-class white people, while less well-off Asian and black people share the health and illness patterns of their white counterparts. There are some exceptions to this – some illnesses are *less* common in *some* minority communities, such as various types of cancer among women (mainly accounted for by lower rates of smoking among Asian women in the past). And *some* illnesses are more common in *some* minority communities – Type 2 diabetes being a case in point. This illness occurs more often among black and South Asian people in the UK irrespective of social class (Taylor and Field, 2007, p. 80).

A second reason for thinking again about the case of Anwar Malik is that his problems might reinforce the impression that getting older inevitably means getting steadily more ill and more disabled. Once we have adopted this pessimistic perspective, it's also easy to assume that intervention often fails to make things better and that therefore some treatments are inappropriate for older people. Mullan (2000), for instance, cites examples where effective medical treatments and rehabilitation therapies are withheld from older people – they are seen as 'not worth it'. So is the pessimistic scenario of health and health care in later life justified in any way?

As you may remember from the work you did in Activity 7, Unit 8, where you looked at data on health and life expectancy from *Social Trends*, the chances of getting a limiting long-term illness do increase steadily as you get older. As well as chronic illness, serious disability affects one in ten of those in the 65–79 age group, but this increases to one in four among those aged 85 or more and to three-quarters of those in care homes (Health Survey for England, 2000). Therefore there is a solid basis for worries about how the health and social care system will cope in the coming decades *if* the number of people with serious disabilities rises in proportion to the fast-rising total of very old people.

The majority of older people are not seriously disabled and lead moderately healthy lives

However, it's worth remembering that if one in four people over the age of 85 has a serious disability, this means that three out of four do not. Most can manage to live fairly independently and in moderate or good health. Gillian Dalley (1998) refers to recent strides in medical treatments that are relatively inexpensive and can greatly improve mobility, sight and other aspects of health. If these continue to develop they will continue to reduce dependency and social care costs. Furthermore, some medical research has shown that older people can recover just as well as younger patients from serious surgical operations. These include such operations as coronary bypass surgery and kidney transplantation (Mullan, 2000). The point here, apart from the very important question of justice and fairness to older service users, is that it is worth spending money on these operations because they are likely to reduce health and social care costs in the longer term.

Neither the pessimistic nor the optimistic scenarios are completely accurate guides to future health trends. In practice, much depends on which sections of the population we want to apply them to. Middle-class and relatively affluent people tend to live longer and are more likely to enjoy a healthy life than people on lower incomes. The 'optimistic scenario' therefore seems more appropriate to people in middle-class positions and above. People with lower incomes, fewer material advantages and perhaps a work history that has adversely affected their health, will more likely (*but not inevitably*) face the pessimistic scenario. In Unit 9 (Section 2), for instance, you saw how the connection between child poverty and low birthweight casts a lifelong shadow over some people's health.

Various studies of social status and patterns of illness have shown that there is a gradual 'class gradient' in health (Marmot, 2004). This means that health inequality is not just a matter of sharp contrasts between the life chances of people at the very top and those at the very bottom of society. Rather, the chances of better health have been found to increase *gradually* the higher up the social scale you are. People in 'middle-middle' class positions, for instance, fare better than those in 'lower-middle' groups, while people in 'upper-middle' positions live longer and tend to be healthier than the group just below them.

Despite government efforts to tackle social exclusion and poverty, there have been few signs of success in tackling the class divide in health (Shaw and Davey Smith, 2005). As you saw earlier in the course, poverty tends to create greater need for both health and social care. The keys to health and independence – for instance, nutrition, quality of care in early childhood, quality of housing and physical environment, education, the type of work we do and income level – all lie outside the walls of the GP surgery, hospital or care home.

Key points

- The *percentage* of older people who will need long-term care in the future is as significant as the gradually rising *total* of people over retirement age.
- Some people think that demand for care services will grow substantially because people are living longer and more medical treatments are available to keep them going.
- A more optimistic view suggests that many older people are healthier now than in previous decades and that this trend will continue.
- It is important to be realistic about the fact that the chances of becoming ill and disabled increase as we age, but not to assume that later life is inevitably a period of steadily declining health for everyone.
- In the UK there are marked health inequalities even though people from most social groups are living longer.
- A rising percentage of those needing long-term health and social care in their seventies and eighties will probably be drawn from the lower-income groups.

3 Social divisions and diversity

As mentioned in Section 1.1, David Coates used the phrase 'patchwork Britain' to summarise the social diversity that had become evident since the 1940s; he also used it to describe the contrasts in housing and living standards in different localities and regions of the UK. He reminded us how these divisions grew wider and more visible in the last quarter of the twentieth century.

3.1 Care and the welfare state in 'patchwork Britain'

Growing social divisions have created a very different society from the one that existed in Beveridge's day. You have only to look at current job advertisements in health and social care to see what today's issues are, and in the next activity you will be able to reflect on this.

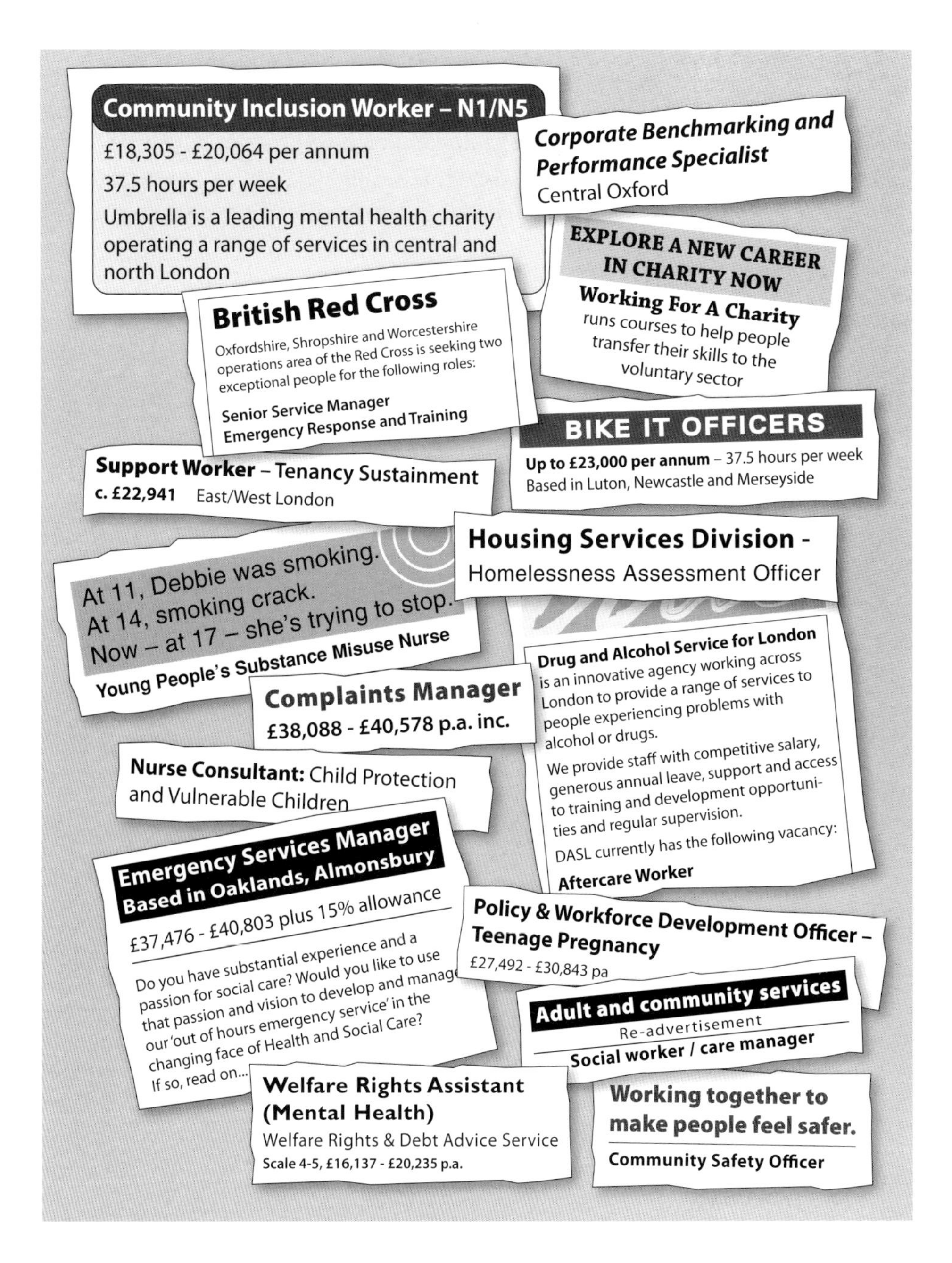

Activity 4 Being William Beveridge: today's welfare state in perspective

Allow about 15 minutes

Look at the advertisements for various jobs in health and social care fields on the previous page. What would William Beveridge have made of them? Imagine you're looking at these job advertisements from his point of view back in the 1940s and write down your reactions to:

(a) the social problems and welfare projects that seem to be preoccupying people in the twenty-first century, as indicated in the advertisements

(b) the kinds of organisations (state, private or voluntary) that are running these projects

(c) the language used in these advertisements to describe the jobs.

Comment

Putting yourself in Beveridge's shoes was just a device to help you to step back from today's welfare state to gain some perspective on it.

(a) Beveridge might have been surprised and disappointed to see that so many social problems seem to have persisted into the twenty-first century. They are illustrated by the advertisements for specialists to tackle, for example, teenage pregnancy, alcohol abuse, inadequate housing and deep-rooted mental health problems. And problems caused by poverty, while seldom referred to explicitly in the advertisements, can be observed in references to welfare rights assistants, debt advice and community renewal officers. Beveridge would probably have hoped that his universal insurance scheme would have been gradually extended and developed in ways that could have eradicated poverty and many other social problems by now.

(b) The space devoted to the voluntary sector and to jobs with charities might have surprised (and perhaps pleased) Beveridge. But although a role was envisaged for the voluntary sector in the post-war welfare state, the more general view was that superior publicly run social services would reduce to a minimum the need for charitable organisations.

(c) Did the sheer complexity of health and social services today strike you? Many advertisements employ jargon and technical terms. For instance, the job requiring a 'Corporate benchmarking and performance specialist' would have bewildered Beveridge (as it did us). For different reasons, the advertisement mentioning 'substance misuse' and 'crack' would have been puzzling to him and it's difficult to know what on earth he would have made of it.

The jobs advertised show how our expectations of what could and should be done to meet people's needs have widened since Beveridge's day. Today's society seems a world away from the time when the welfare state was launched in the 1940s. Basic problems such as poverty still exist, but care services face a world that has become more complicated, diverse, fragmented and unequal than it was.

On the other hand, however, the UK today seems in some ways to be *less* class-divided by comparison with the ordered, hierarchical world of the 1950s (Hennessy, 2007). Surely health and social care now take place in an atmosphere that is more democratic and less snobbish or 'hung up' about the 'niceties' of social status and social class compared with the 'old days'? Anti-discrimination and equality legislation shows a commitment to giving everyone an equal start in life irrespective of their background, and politicians and leading public figures want to appear classless in the way they talk and in how they appear. Given all this, is it really correct to say that the UK has become a more divided and unequal society in recent decades?

Dining at the Café Royal, London, 1953

Glasgow cigarette factory, 1955

Have inequalities increased since the 1950s?

Ex-Etonian David Cameron was chosen as leader of the Conservative Party in 2005. Like other political leaders, he wanted to present himself from the start as the classless 'ordinary guy' or 'family man'.

3.2 Inequality, poverty and social exclusion: have they really increased?

Despite the *appearance* of being a less class-divided society, the UK has in fact become steadily more unequal in terms of wealth and income. In the 1980s and 1990s, *inequality* grew as fast as poverty. The incomes of the top 10 per cent of earners, for instance, rose by 62 per cent in real value between 1979 and 1992. The incomes of the bottom 10 per cent actually fell in real value in the 1980s (Coates, 2005). Why has this happened?

Between the 1940s and the 1970s the welfare state demonstrated that through taxation and welfare policies, substantial reductions in poverty and inequality could be made. So although the UK of the 1970s had plenty of inequalities, relative to the present day (and to other societies in Western Europe), it was more equal. It was when taxation and welfare policies were changed by Margaret Thatcher's government (with widespread public support) in the 1980s, in a way that benefited richer rather than poorer people, that inequality soared. Looking back, it's clear that income inequality would have grown even faster after 1980 but for the 'braking' effect of the welfare state and social security.

Poverty is not just *one* 'thing' or problem, and that is why it has proved to be one of the most difficult problems the welfare state has had to deal with. As you know from Block 3, 'poverty' is actually an umbrella term for a wide variety of complex experiences and circumstances. The problems faced by low-income families on the Thornhill Estate (described in Unit 9) illustrate this point. There was some limited success in tackling poverty after 2000 – for instance, the government in office between 2001 and 2005 didn't meet its child poverty targets, but it did make significant progress in this direction (Toynbee and Walker, 2005).

Relative poverty means being unable to afford the things that most of us see as essential to playing a full part in social or family life. Not being able to afford to take a family holiday could be classed as being in poverty in today's society, although Beveridge and others in the 1940s wouldn't have accepted this definition. As the majority become better and better off, expectations of what is 'essential' rise too. But many children in relatively poor households:

> … never go on a summer holiday and have no money for swimming, [never] have a birthday party or a sleepover or take school trips, let alone own a computer or a mobile phone.
>
> (Toynbee, 2006a, p. 39)

One strategy to reduce relative poverty among children in families like this is to maximise the family income through policies that, among other things, regularly up-rate minimum wages, tax credits and social security benefit payments. Channelling more money towards individuals would have helped carers such as Ann (see Unit 1). But is simply putting more money into the pockets of people such as Simon (whom you met in Unit 10) helpful?

Activity 5 Would more money help Simon?

Allow about 10 minutes

Read through the box below to remind yourself about the distinctions between poverty and social exclusion. Then think back to Block 3, Unit 10 where you were introduced to Simon and his situation. Now write down a brief answer to the following question:

Would giving Simon more money or increasing his benefits be sufficient to lift him out of poverty or to improve his life?

Poverty and social exclusion: a reminder

Don't forget that poverty and social exclusion are *overlapping* concepts that often describe the same situations or problems. Many of the people who are described as being 'poor' or on low incomes also experience social exclusion in some way – and vice versa. Also, many of the solutions or strategies that are suggested for reducing poverty are the same as those aimed at reducing social exclusion. However, there are some differences in *emphasis* between the two concepts (see Section 2 of Unit 9).

Poverty	**Social exclusion**
Lack of money and other resources (housing, clothes, etc.)	Lack of opportunity through exclusion from the mainstream – those who are excluded are disconnected from, or rejected by, the rest of society: they can't easily 'join in' or retrain
Can occur whether in work or not	Mainly refers to people who are excluded from the labour market or are unemployed
Remedy: maximise incomes of low-income individuals and families; boost welfare rights; raise welfare benefits or tax credits	*Remedy*: maximise inclusion through better education, training and work opportunities; invest in childcare to free up working parents; anti-discrimination policies to penalise exclusion or dismissal from work

Comment

Perhaps you thought, like us, that there were several strong reasons why someone like Simon would be unable to make good use of extra cash benefits without some additional intervention or help. He didn't seem to have the skills to live independently or to manage money very well. He was also in a state of mental and emotional turmoil, heard voices and was isolated. For various reasons, this could have led to him being exploited or robbed of any extra cash that came his way (remember that he was beaten up several times).

Lifting 'hard-to-reach' people like Simon out of poverty requires a range of anti-poverty strategies. As argued in Unit 10, Simon is experiencing *social exclusion*. Anti-poverty strategies that address social exclusion are based on the idea of strengthening the social networks and community involvement of those who are excluded. Simon lacked a cohesive, supportive social network – he was isolated and had few, if any, reliable relationships with relatives or friends.

There were signs that, as with targets to reduce child poverty, government policy from the end of the 1990s onwards had made some headway in tackling social exclusion (Pierson, 2002). This was done by applying a wide range of community development strategies, such as introducing children's centres that were targeted at areas of particular social disadvantage. But despite these efforts, the overall picture of the UK as a 'patchwork' society of widening differences and divisions remains.

3.3 Growing racial and ethnic diversity

Coates picked growing racial and ethnic diversity as one of the more significant social trends in the UK today. You were introduced to the topic of ethnic diversity and its implications in Unit 11. There are members of minority ethnic groups in almost every urban and rural area of the UK. Some minorities – notably Chinese – are dispersed, mainly as a result of the restaurant trade or being in professional occupations such as medicine or law. However, despite the rising number of migrants from European Union countries in Eastern Europe, large tracts of the country – particularly rural Wales, Scotland, Northern Ireland and north-west and south-west England – have been called 'the white highlands' and are still not very ethnically or racially diverse. This can present tricky problems for those charged with the task of providing a full range of culturally sensitive services in these areas, because there might be only a few people from various minority communities needing care services. Culturally sensitive services, as you will recall from Unit 11, are adapted in terms of the languages, dietary requirements and religious and cultural backgrounds of each minority. In the next activity you will consider the importance of such services.

Activity 6 Ethnic and racial diversity: why is it an issue for everyone?

Allow about 10 minutes

Imagine you live in an area in which there are very small numbers of people from a minority ethnic community. Write down the reasons why you think it remains important to ensure that culturally appropriate care services are available.

Comment

It does require expense and commitment to provide specially adapted health and social care services when only a few people are ever likely to need them at any one time. But there is a parallel to be drawn here with the requirements of disabled people and the fact that local authorities and other organisations have to ensure that services and facilities are suitably adapted. Thus, there is a strong case for saying that the issue of numbers should not come into it. When people live in very small or scattered minority communities, their need for care and support might be greater, or more urgent, than in more concentrated minority communities where local support networks are more likely to exist. This is why ethnic diversity is an issue for everyone – and for every community or part of the UK – not just for inner-city areas in which many minority ethnic communities are concentrated.

You might also have argued that people from minority ethnic groups in the UK do enjoy certain rights under current equality legislation. As you saw in Unit 11, discrimination is sometimes about not acting or not providing services that everyone can use. So if a local authority or health trust fails to provide culturally appropriate services, that public body could face legal action or complaints that it was indirectly discriminating on ethnic or racial grounds.

The UK's black and Asian minority communities have tended to be concentrated in the larger cities and towns. The growing numbers of migrants from Eastern Europe are more dispersed, moving into rural areas and regions that hitherto haven't seen many immigrants. Despite all these changes, however, many people in the majority population – including those working in the care services – do not necessarily have a good understanding of minority communities. This is one reason why the contribution of minorities to staffing the caring services is so important.

In 2008, the Federation of Poles in Great Britain 'reluctantly' contacted the Press Complaints Commission accusing the *Daily Mail* of defaming Polish residents in Britain through its headlines and articles such as these

Similarly, knowledge of care services – and of life in 'white Britain' generally – can also be sketchy among sections of some minority communities. Research carried out in Birmingham, for instance, revealed a high proportion of older women in the Pakistani and Bangladeshi communities who couldn't speak English and knew very little about the social care services that were available (Blakemore and Boneham, 1994). It is possible, but not at all certain, that in time these gaps in understanding between the minorities and the majority will be closed.

Key points

- Despite a rising standard of living for most, the UK is a highly unequal society in which the gap between the affluent two-thirds and the relatively poor one-third is getting wider.
- The welfare state and various social policies have had only limited success in containing a rise in relative poverty and social exclusion.
- The UK has become more racially and ethnically diverse than it was.
- All these trends are resulting in a more complicated, diverse society in which the idea of providing similar or common care services for all is becoming more problematic.
- For a variety of reasons, relations between the white majority and *some* minorities are problematic and are marred by a mutual lack of understanding.

4 Choice and control

You will recall from the previous unit that Conservative governments were strongly influenced by New Right ideas, which stressed the importance of trying to cut public spending and the taxes to fund it. After its election in 1997, Labour broke away from the policy of continually squeezing public services, but in other ways it carried on from where the Conservatives had left off. Tony Blair's governments (1997–2007) put an increasing emphasis on what he called the 'modernisation' of care services. This involved a government drive towards more competition between service providers and an even greater role for the private and voluntary sectors in delivering services. It is not hard to see the continuing influence of New Right ideas in these policies.

In this section, we are going to focus on how governments since 2000 have approached issues related to choice and control. Should we be free to make our own choices regarding our individual needs or should the government be held responsible for ensuring fairness all round? We will start with the global context. No country can run its services in isolation from the rest of the world. There are always pressures and influences from outside, as we discuss below.

4.1 The global context

In 2006 there was a major controversy about the decision by the National Institute for Health and Clinical Excellence (NICE) that people in the early stages of Alzheimer's disease should not get a medicine called Aricept (produced by Pfizer and a Japanese company, Eisai) on the NHS. Rival treatments, such as Reminyl, produced by Shire, were also ruled out. NICE is an independent organisation that was set up to provide guidance on new medicines and treatments and whether they should be available on the NHS. If NICE decides that a medicine cannot be prescribed by NHS doctors, the big pharmaceutical companies, such as Pfizer and Glaxo, cannot sell them on a large scale through the NHS.

But was NICE justified in its decision about Aricept, and does NICE work in the interests of people who need care? In the next activity you will be able to compare rival views on this question. First read the following views and then complete the activity that follows.

> … our concerns lie with the transparency and fairness of the NICE process and the delay it causes patients in gaining access to new medicines, even when proven to be clinically- and cost-effective.
>
> (Andrew Hotchkiss, Chair, American Pharmaceutical Group, Letters, *Guardian*, 17 November 2006)

> There is no question of anyone bypassing the clear processes which are used to evaluate new drugs for use in the NHS … Sometimes NICE has to say no to a treatment because the evidence does not support it as being clinically- and cost-effective. These are not easy recommendations for anybody to make and we recognise that when this happens there are implications for patients and their carers – not just drugs companies. But it is the fairest way in an environment where resources are limited.
>
> (Andy Burnham MP, Health Minister, Letters, *Guardian*, 17 November 2006)

> I think they [NICE] are not being tough enough.
>
> Industry has had high profits and high prices but has been very disappointing over the last several years bringing new treatments to market that are cost effective, and now they are trying to undermine Nice.
>
> (Alan Maynard, Professor of Health Economics, University of York, quoted in Barriaux and Boseley, 2006)

> Aricept has been just marvellous. I had been going downhill in mental capacity for 18 months. I knew that it was very similar to my mother and at exactly the same age … I can see how lucky I've been – how Aricept has restored my life and given me time to reorganise and rethink.
>
> (71-year-old woman with Alzheimer's disease taking Aricept, Rutland, quoted in Alzheimer's Society, 2004, p. 2)

> Taking Aricept has enabled my wife to have, to a large extent, a more or less normal life. The consultant who monitored progress, applying the standard tests, was satisfied that Aricept had been instrumental in slowing down the effects of the disease.
>
> (84-year-old carer, London, quoted in Alzheimer's Society, 2004, p. 28)

> [NICE's] [d]ecisions are made by panels of 30 people – including doctors, scientists, NHS managers, nurses and patients – who examine the research evidence in scrupulous detail …
>
> But … [f]aced with patients clinging to any last straw, the big questions remain … How good a quality of life should be saved, at what price, for how long? … Nice has to consider what better treatments could be bought for how many others for the cost of holding off death for a few more painful months?
>
> (Toynbee, 2006b)

Activity 7 NICE and the drug companies

Allow about 10 minutes

After comparing the comments given above, do you think the pharmaceutical companies might have a case for restricting the authority of NICE to decide which medicines will be prescribed on the NHS, and to have a freer market in the UK in which to sell their products? Write down your thoughts on this, with at least one point for and one against.

Comment

NICE's decision in 2006 not to approve Aricept and similar medicines for NHS treatment of people in the early stages of Alzheimer's disease raised some particularly difficult questions. These treatments do seem to help many patients (but not all), not only helping them to do more for themselves, but also relieving their carers and restoring some fulfilment to their lives. The decision not to make Aricept and the other medicines available on the NHS was very disappointing, if not devastating, for them and for their pressure group, the Alzheimer's Society. But as Polly Toynbee concludes, it's not as simple as that. When the money to pay for treatments is limited – and it has limits in all health care systems, not just the NHS in the UK – paying a lot for one new treatment can mean not being able to pay for something else that might be even more beneficial to another patient group.

So in the end the argument seems to boil down to two alternatives: either a return to the pre-1999 situation in which there was a freer market for the drug companies and more of a 'postcode lottery' (some new medicines available on the NHS in some areas but not others, depending on the funds available); or having an independent watchdog such as NICE, which makes the fact that we have to ration health care treatment more transparent and is fairer overall, but which can seem very unfair to particular patient groups.

Whether NICE survives is a test of how far the NHS can act as a buffer against the lobbying power of multinational companies, which represent the influences of globalisation in health care. Australia once had a watchdog similar to the UK's NICE but, according to Maynard (2006), it became bogged down in a series of protracted and expensive legal challenges to its decisions by multinational drug companies, rendering it ineffective.

The drugs industry is a good example of a global business. Most of the leading pharmaceutical companies are based in the USA but operate throughout the world and are very large in terms of their wealth and scale. For instance, Pfizer, the world's biggest drug company in 2006, had 'revenue of US$52 billion (£28 billion) and a net income of over US$11 billion' in 2004 (Evans and Boseley, 2006). However, the UK's NHS is also a huge financial operation. In a single year (2006), for instance, it cost in the region of £95 billion to run the NHS (Office for National Statistics, 2008). International drug companies are drawn to this very sizeable market. And it follows that they have a strong interest in trying to reduce any restrictions on their ability to sell freely in the UK market. The pressures exerted by multinational drug companies therefore illustrate the impact of globalisation on health care.

'Globalisation' has become a widely used term in recent years, but what exactly is it and why is it becoming an increasingly important influence on health and social care?

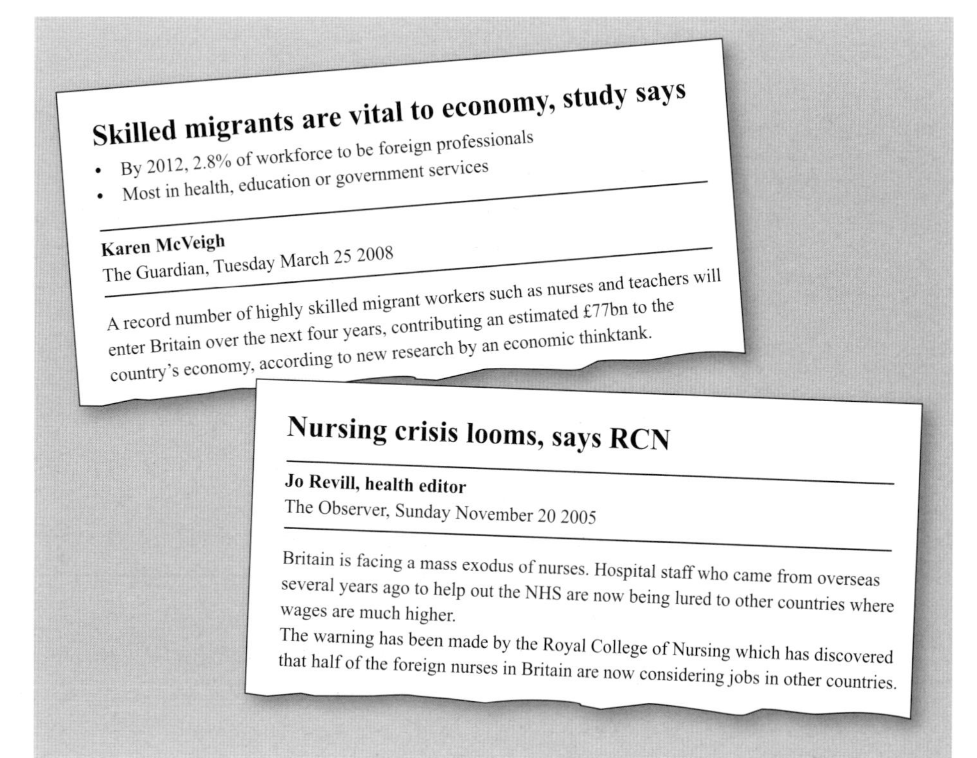

Skilled migrants are vital to economy, study says

- By 2012, 2.8% of workforce to be foreign professionals
- Most in health, education or government services

Karen McVeigh
The Guardian, Tuesday March 25 2008

A record number of highly skilled migrant workers such as nurses and teachers will enter Britain over the next four years, contributing an estimated £77bn to the country's economy, according to new research by an economic thinktank.

Nursing crisis looms, says RCN

Jo Revill, health editor
The Observer, Sunday November 20 2005

Britain is facing a mass exodus of nurses. Hospital staff who came from overseas several years ago to help out the NHS are now being lured to other countries where wages are much higher.
The warning has been made by the Royal College of Nursing which has discovered that half of the foreign nurses in Britain are now considering jobs in other countries.

Activity 8 The 'globalisation' of care

Allow about 10 minutes

Read through the definition of globalisation in the box below. You have already seen how the provision of drug treatments in the NHS illustrates the impact of globalisation on health care. Can you think of other examples of the impact of globalisation on health or social care? Note down your ideas.

Globalisation

'Global' means the whole world and 'globalisation' literally means to make global. It is an umbrella term referring to a number of rapid changes that are sweeping the world, bringing about a form of international integration. We can spot these worldwide influences everywhere, from the low cost of the T-shirt or electrical item we want to buy (often made in India or the Far East) to the spread of the internet and global brands such as McDonald's and Starbucks. The driving force in this process is *economic* globalisation. The world's goods and services are increasingly produced in a uniform way and on a global scale. The largest international businesses and companies operate on a worldwide stage and want to export to free markets in as many countries as possible.

Comment

Globalisation can also be seen in:

- The *globalisation of the job market* – for instance, the steady rise in the numbers of health workers coming to work in the NHS, such as Dr Moonsawmy and Dr Jacobs whom you read about in Unit 21, or leaving the NHS to work abroad. Migrant workers are also important as a source of labour in the care home and home care industries.
- The *globalisation of services* can be seen in the growing number of people in the UK who are prepared to 'shop around' for quicker, cheaper or better treatment in other countries, such as dental treatment in the Czech Republic, cataract operations in India or cosmetic surgery in South Africa.
- The *globalisation of finance and investment* can be seen in the way in which big companies such as HealthNet, for instance, have been moving into the UK to provide fast-track surgical treatment centres for the NHS. A similar trend can be observed in social care. For example, overseas companies have been buying firms that provide home care in the UK and providing financial backing for sheltered accommodation developments for older people.

To summarise, globalisation represents a wide range of influences on the UK and on health and social care policy. However, it would be wrong to see globalisation as an all-pervasive or completely dominant influence. Governments can still decide to go their own way to a large extent in the decisions they take over health and social care issues.

4.2 Central control

Although the UK government continued the push towards having a variety of service providers, it did not want there to be too much variety in the *standards* of health and social care to be provided, or in *forms* of care (i.e. the ways in which services were to be delivered). This meant putting in place new policies and systems to control and regulate the service providers. For example, in Unit 19 you read about the use of protocols in the health service as a way of regulating and standardising practice. In the field of social care, the protection of children and vulnerable adults from abuse in care settings is a further example of the way in which government policy and tightening regulations are affecting day-to-day care practice. Indeed, the whole issue of collecting information to check quality and standards, which you read about in Block 5, is symptomatic of the trend towards central control in care policy – or, as many managers and care workers at the front line of services might put it, increasing 'interference' from above.

Think back to Unit 21 and the community care and health service reforms of the 1990s. These reforms contained a tension between, on one hand, the government's determination to remain in control and ensure that the same reforms happened in every area and, on the other, its desire to encourage competition between different service providers, to take account of local variation in needs and choice for service users.

The box below includes some examples of regulatory bodies for health and social care, which were introduced in England by Labour just before and after the year 2000. They illustrate the government's drive to centralise and standardise the way in which care is delivered, in an attempt to overcome the effects of the 'postcode lottery'. It is important to bear in mind, however, that at the same time Scotland and Wales (and later Northern Ireland, after 2007) were developing their own policies on health and social care as a result of devolution. We will come back to this shortly.

Health and social care in England: examples of control from the centre

Some government policies in health care which were introduced by the Labour governments stood out as being particularly 'centralising'. They included, for instance:

- **National Service Frameworks (NSFs)**. These guidelines lay down centrally what the best or optimum treatment should be and how health services can best be deployed to meet various needs (e.g. in mental health).
- **The National Institute for Health and Clinical Excellence (NICE)**. This was set up in 1999. As with National Service Frameworks, its aim was to reduce the 'postcode lottery' effect, where some treatments are available in certain areas but not in others.
- **The Commission for Social Care Inspection (CSCI)**. This regulates and inspects social care provision against national minimum care standards and assesses the performance of local social services providers against performance indicators.
- **The Healthcare Commission**. This inspects primary health care and hospitals. It ranks them through league tables and awards stars according to performance. At the time of writing, plans were announced to create a new watchdog, the Care Quality Commission (Ofcare), which would merge the Healthcare Commission, CSCI and the Mental Health Act Commission into a single health and social care inspectorate – suggesting yet more centralisation.
- **A series of national plans for the health service**. These illustrate the power of central government (rather than the doctors or the health service itself) to set the agenda. As long-term plans, they indicated a commitment to the continuation of the NHS, rather than a switch to a private health care system or a European-style health service funded by social insurance.

The advantages of more regulation and central control are that the government can more easily:

- iron out unfairness or inequalities between different areas, or between different services
- guarantee quality of care by setting targets and enforcing common standards; this helps to enhance service users' rights and their ability to choose between different services or care providers
- hold local agencies and managers of services accountable for failure to deliver a good enough service
- check that money is being spent to good effect.

But what are the disadvantages of this approach?

Activity 9 Control from the centre: the down side?

Allow about 15 minutes

Write down *two* drawbacks you can think of to having more central government control and regulation of health and social care services. To help you, think back to Unit 19 and Reader Chapter 20 by Rebecca Lawton and Dianne Parker, where you read about people's views of using protocols in health care.

Do you think the disadvantages outweigh the advantages listed above?

Comment

The example of protocols indirectly raises the issue of who should be in control of health care and how much leeway health care staff should have without 'interference' from above. We thought that some of the main drawbacks of trying to strengthen control from the centre were:

- Demoralisation among managers and frontline staff struggling to cope with an endless stream of government reforms and restructuring of services.
- A target-driven, 'tick-box' culture that encourages practitioners to put bureaucratic performance before people's needs. Practitioners might begin to feel that they are no longer allowed the scope to use their individual expertise and judgement. This might in turn seem to devalue professional pride in solving problems or creating new solutions.
- The production of information and statistics that conform to government requirements, but which do not give an accurate picture of what is actually happening on the ground. Frontline workers and managers find ways round the targets they are set.
- A lack of democracy. It is harder for the voice of the public or the service user to be heard in a centralised, managerial system.

Few would dispute the importance of trying to achieve fairness, quality and accountability, but the issue is whether the means of accomplishing these goals work.

It might seem odd to be pointing out a trend towards centralisation when the opposite was also happening – that is, the emergence of greater variation and differences in the NHS and social care across the UK. However, devolution has not meant that care services in Scotland, Wales and Northern Ireland have escaped the trend towards centralisation and UK government restructuring. Rather, they have experienced centralisation *in their own ways* since devolution.

We will have a closer look at the impact of devolution next.

4.3 Devolved control

Despite globalisation and the pressures towards uniformity, significantly different approaches in health and social care policies have emerged in the UK since Scotland, Wales and, later, Northern Ireland gained some autonomy through devolved government. What these differences demonstrate is that there are choices to be made about how we want our services to be provided. Alvarez-Rosete et al. (2005) make this point, as well as providing a useful summary of the devolution process. They were writing before devolved powers were restored in Northern Ireland in 2007 following an election to the Assembly and formation of a new power-sharing government:

> [NHS] [r]eforms have come and gone, but until the late 1990s they had been applied similarly across the four countries of the UK … However, in 1998 the Labour government devolved power to an elected parliament in Scotland, an elected assembly in Wales, and, until it was suspended in 2002, an elected assembly in Northern Ireland.
>
> Although the powers of each political body differ, each has important freedoms with respect to NHS policy. As a result, in England, the emphasis has been on national targets to improve performance (particularly reducing waiting times), increasing capacity, and sharper market-style incentives. In Scotland, the 1990s quasi-market has been abolished and steps taken to build a professionally led, integrated system based on concepts such as managed clinical networks. In Wales, the focus has been on improving public health through partnership working between the local NHS, local government, and communities, and in Northern Ireland, developments have been stalled by political uncertainty.
>
> (Alvarez-Rosete et al., 2005, p. 946)

The aim of the next activity is to give you a chance to get your own impression of the types of change that have taken place as a result of devolution and of the ways in which care policies are diverging across the UK. It will also remind you that the HSC Resource Bank could be a useful resource when you are studying or researching particular topics in the future.

Activity 10 Comparing care policies in the UK

Allow about 30 minutes

Through the course website, find the HSC Resource Bank, which is listed under Resources. On the home page, under 'Browse HSC Resources' follow the link to the 'Care Systems and Structures' section. Scroll down the page and click on 'Wales'. Under 'Regulation of Care' you will find an alphabetical listing – look for Older People's Commissioner for Wales and open the link. The Commissioner (created in 2006) was appointed in April 2008. Here you can use the link to find out more about the job of Older People's Commissioner and how it might be having an impact on care standards, quality or other aspects of older people's welfare.

When you have done that, go back to the 'Care Systems and Structures' page and follow the link for *another* part of the UK (England, Northern Ireland or Scotland). Now do the same again – look for anything that corresponds to the role of Older People's Commissioner. Does this post exist in the other countries you have chosen to look at?

Comment

At the time of writing, Wales was the only country in the UK to have an Older People's Commissioner – in fact, the only country in the world to have such an office. (Incidentally, Wales also led the way in being the first country in the UK to have a Children's Commissioner.)

By the time you are reading this, perhaps Older People's Commissioners will have been appointed in England or Northern Ireland or Scotland. How much difference having such a Commissioner will make to standards or quality of care in Wales remains to be seen, and you might have been able to find some views or evidence about this by using the links on the Older People's Commissioner for Wales website to the Commissioner's reports to the National Assembly Government. But whatever the evidence, the fact that one country pioneered the idea of having an Older People's Commissioner illustrates the basic point that devolution is bringing up all kinds of differences and innovations in care policy.

Table 1 provides a round-up of the key differences in health and social care services between the different countries of the UK in 2008. Inevitably, it is an over-simplification of the reality. For example, although free personal care is not universally available in Wales, some Welsh local authorities provide free personal health and social care, without means testing, for up to six weeks in any one year. Likewise, local authorities in Scotland vary in the rules governing assessment and eligibility for free care. Although free dental check-ups are not universally available in Wales, they are available for everyone aged under 25 or over 60.

Table 1 Health and social care: how countries in the UK compare (2008)

	England	**Wales**	**Scotland**	**N. Ireland**
Free personal care for all	NO	NO	YES	NO
Purchaser–provider split	YES	YES	NO	YES
Foundation hospitals	YES	NO	NO	NO
Private sector used to finance new facilities and reduce waiting times	YES	YES	YES	YES
Private sector used to provide mainstream health care services	YES	NO	NO	NO
NHS waiting times improved after devolution	YES	NO	NO	NO
Free prescriptions for all	NO	YES	YES	NO
Free NHS sight tests for all	NO	NO	YES	NO
Free dental check-ups for all	NO	NO	YES	NO

Despite the caveats, what these differences mean in practice is very important. We will explore this point in the next activity.

Activity 11 Living in Scotland: Angus and Ann

Allow about 15 minutes

Think back to the story of Angus and his stepdaughter Ann, which you read about and listened to when you were studying Block 1. You may recall that they lived in Scotland.

Then look back at Table 1, which outlines how health and social care compares across the four countries of the UK. If you made any notes for the last activity have a look at those too.

Now, suppose that Angus has been in hospital for a hip replacement operation. He had to wait a considerable time for this operation, but is now due to be discharged. Ann has not been well herself and has arranged for him to go into a care home for a few weeks before returning back home.

What difference will living in Scotland make for Angus and Ann?

Comment

You may have noted first of all that there is a good chance that Angus will not have to pay for his personal care while he is in the care home. Had he lived in Wales he might have been entitled to six weeks' free personal care. By contrast, in England, for example, he would have been subjected to a means test and, as a result, may have had to pay.

There are other things you may have noted. For example, had Angus lived in England, he may not have had to wait so long for his operation because England, unlike Northern Ireland, Scotland or Wales, has focused on reducing waiting times. Something else you may have noted is that Ann, who is not yet 60, is entitled to free prescriptions and dental and eye checks – whether or not she is in receipt of a carer's allowance.

While the finer detail of the differences between the four nations is complex, what the above activity demonstrates is the increasing divergence of care policies in the UK and the implications of these for service users. Scotland stands out as being more strongly committed to publicly provided services and has rejected the development of an internal market. This has meant that the trend towards individual care budgets and the use of Direct Payments is less developed in Scotland. This is something we will now turn to.

4.4 Individual control

There was a growing realisation that the community care reforms introduced in the 1990s – which had done much to stimulate the voluntary and private care sectors – did not bring the degree of independence and choice that had been envisaged for service users. As in the NHS internal market, social services users found that, instead of making their own decisions about their care, choices were often made on their behalf by social workers and care workers. Disabled people in particular wanted more control over their own care or support arrangements. Direct Payments and, more recently, Individual Budgets were developed to give users greater involvement in choosing the services they need and in having a say in the design and delivery of services.

Direct Payments, which you may remember reading about in Unit 3, Section 5, were first introduced through the Direct Payments Act 1996. They are a sum of money paid to people who have been assessed as being eligible for care services so that they can purchase and arrange their own personal assistance. Direct Payments were introduced slowly, initially just for adults of working age. They were extended to older people in 2000 and, a year later, to carers, parents of disabled children and 16–17-year-olds. As Reader Chapter 8 by Tim Stainton and Steve Boyce, which you read in Unit 3, demonstrates, Direct Payments have been very popular with some people. However, take-up has been low and uneven among different user groups and between different local authority areas. By March 2007, 48,000 adults aged over the age of 18 living in England were receiving a Direct Payment, 64 per cent of whom were aged between 18 and 64 (DH, 2007). The highest take-up was among younger adults with physical or sensory impairments and with learning disabilities. The lowest take-up was among people with mental health problems and older people (Commission for Social Care Inspection, 2008).

Activity 12 Taking up Direct Payments

Allow about 10 minutes

Bearing in mind that over two-thirds of people assessed as needing social care services are older people, why do you think the take-up of Direct Payments among this user group has been so low? Note down some reasons you can think of. Also note down reasons why you think take-up among people using mental health services is so low.

If you want to remind yourself of the pros and cons of employing a personal assistant, look back to Section 5 of Unit 3.

Comment

You may well have decided that, as with most things, there is no single explanation. The initial exclusion of older people of course means that use among them got off to a slower start. In Unit 3 it was suggested that social workers and care managers may underestimate the abilities and capacities of some people to use and manage Direct Payments and to choose and employ a personal assistant. However, as also pointed out in Unit 3, organisations are developing to help people with the practical issues involved. So while the undervaluing of people's abilities may well be a factor, there is also evidence that some people do not want to take on the responsibilities of care managers or the potential risks attached to employing (unregulated) personal assistants.

A report by the Commission for Social Care Inspection in England (2004) identified the following reasons for low take-up of Direct Payments:

- lack of information for service users
- lack of awareness among staff of what Direct Payments have to offer
- undervaluing people's abilities to manage a Direct Payment
- inadequate arrangements for supporting Direct Payment users with administrative and other issues
- too much paperwork.

All these issues can be overcome. What is less easy to overcome is the reluctance on the part of service users to take on the responsibility of a Direct Payment, and it was in response to this reluctance that the idea of Individual Budgets was mooted. These provide for more flexibility. Drawing on a variety of funding streams, a budget is allocated to an individual service user who can then choose to take it as a cash payment, as services (excluding permanent residential care) or as a mixture of both. By March 2008, 3871 people had an Individual Budget (Henwood, 2008).

The key principles behind personalised care, which encompasses Individual Budgets and self-directed support, are user control, choice of service and flexibility of support (Henwood and Hudson, 2007). As Henwood and Hudson (2007) point out, this move towards personalised care is 'not so much an extension of Direct Payments as a shift in the paradigm that underpins how we think about the relationship between citizen and state in respect of welfare services and support'. It is a move right away from the universalist, 'one-size-fits-all' approach to a system that claims to respond to the diverse individual needs and demands that characterise the UK in the twenty-first century.

Key points

- Globalisation represents a powerful set of influences on both health and social care, although these influences can be controlled to some extent by independent bodies such as NICE.
- Governments after 1997 put a lot of emphasis on trying to control health and social care services from the centre. A target-driven culture developed, with a lot more regulation and inspection of care standards taking place.
- Devolution is bringing about a trend towards growing differences in care policy within the UK.
- The introduction of Direct Payments and Individual Budgets, aimed at putting the 'consumer' or service user in control of services, began in a slow and gradual way, but personalisation looks set to become a very important feature of twenty-first-century care.

5 Social care: Cinderella still waiting?

The history of social care, as we pointed out in Unit 21, shows that social care services have long been regarded as the 'Cinderella' of the welfare state. In a twenty-first-century context, is this picture of social care still accurate? It's certainly true that social services didn't receive the big increases in public spending that benefited the NHS in the first decade, although a substantial rise of 6 per cent per year (above inflation) was budgeted for between 2004 and 2008 (Netten, 2005). And social care has not been standing still since 2000 – far from it. The policy context has been one of constant change and restructuring by government, as in the health service.

5.1 Financial uncertainty

Despite the moves towards giving service users more control over their own care, genuine user involvement, democratic experiments in new ways of running services and user choice are hard to achieve in a climate of financial uncertainty and council cutbacks. Unfortunately, financial crisis was as much a part of the context of social care in the years after 2000 as it was in the years before:

> Squeezed between central spending targets and councils with other things to spend available money on (or palliate council tax payers by cutting spending) social services departments were often the losers. Unlike the NHS there were no promises from prime ministers sitting on sofas in television studios, no golden commitments from the Treasury. Personal social services spending was rising and Labour could boast that 14 percent more hours of domiciliary care were provided in the eight years from 1997, but that was grossly misleading. To save on the NHS bill, people were being discharged from hospital in worse physical condition and local social services had then to concentrate resources on the frailest.
>
> (Toynbee and Walker, 2005, pp. 35–6)

The experiences of Lynda Wisbach, a part-time civil servant and carer from Newcastle, illustrate the impact of the continuing trend in financial cutbacks after 2005:

> Newcastle used to have a fantastic record on services for vulnerable people, but things have deteriorated in the last couple of years. The council says it does not get enough money from the government so had cut the social services budget. My respite care has been cut [and] … the council didn't tell us about the cut, and didn't do an assessment, which, by law, it is meant to do before cutting a care package … I rely on that package of care to enable me to work … They are desperate to keep council tax down. I tell people that home help will disappear, but they don't believe me. Nobody notices the crisis in social care till it happens to them.
>
> (Quoted in Butler, 2007, p. 3)

In order to put this in context, take a look at the following extract from an article by David Brindle (2007) and complete the next activity.

Families told elderly care crisis looming

David Brindle

The Guardian, Wednesday 10 January 2007

Families face a growing burden of care for elderly and disabled relatives and most people will have to pay for their own support services in old age as the state's role shrinks, the government's care watchdog will warn today.

A fundamental shift in responsibility is taking place as councils respond to spiralling demand by concentrating resources on fewer people with greater needs, the Commission for Social Care Inspection will say in a report.

Dame Denise Platt, who chairs the commission, is expected to say that older people in much of England can anticipate no help from the state until their needs are judged "critical". Her report will urge fresh thinking on the help given to families in what will be the first high-level recognition of a trend across the country.

Dame Denise will warn that at the moment people without family or friends able or willing to help them, or without the means to buy in care, are being left to cope as best they can.

She will say that responsibility should not be passed over in this way without a proper infrastructure in place to enable people to find alternative sources of care and to offer greater support for family carers. She will call on ministers to acknowledge the realities and to negotiate a new "pact" between state and individual.

The crisis in care services reflects the growing longevity of disabled people, often with high support needs, but mainly the swelling elderly population. The number of people aged 65 and over is projected to increase by more than 80% to almost 17 million in the first half of this century; the number of those 85 and over is expected to double to more than 1.8 million by 2028.

The impact of this on the care system was highlighted last year by an unofficial report by a team led by Sir Derek Wanless, who calculated that spending on personal care for older people would have to treble to £30bn a year over the next two decades to maintain the status quo. Critics believe ministers have filed the Wanless recommendations for reform of care funding in the "too difficult" basket and hopes are not high of a significant boost for social care in the forthcoming three-year spending review. But developments on the ground have brought issues to a head.

While debate about Wanless has focused on residential care - where more than 30% of people are now paying some or all their fees of £400 a week in care homes and £600 in nursing homes - a growing outcry has been prompted by restrictions placed by councils on services for people remaining in their own homes.

Two in three English councils now limit home care, such as assistance with dressing, washing and cooking, to people with needs assessed as "critical" or "substantial". Most councils expect to tighten these criteria further this year. According to the Local Government Association, help currently provided to up to 370,000 people with assessed lower-level needs will disappear altogether by 2009. In a joint letter published in the Guardian shortly before Christmas, leaders of 45 councils warned that "services for the elderly are now teetering on the brink. The present situation is unsustainable."

What particularly worries the care inspectorate is that many people are unaware of what is happening and have unrealistic expectations. A recent survey for the LGA found a third of adults thought they would automatically get free home care in their old age and only 10% thought they would have to pay for it entirely from their own pocket.

The inspectorate will today say councils are acting sensibly in rationing support, and are getting better at accurately assessing needs. But it will also say that many councils are doing little to help those who have to find their own care, at average charges of more than £10 an hour. This echoes a report published this week by care advice charity Counsel and Care, which warned of a widening “care gap” between people's needs and available services and called for measures including appointment of independent care advisers in every community and creation of a national care advice service.

(Source: Brindle, 2007, p. 1)

Activity 13 Why the continuing crisis in social care?

Allow about 10 minutes

In Section 2 of this unit, we pointed out that it's possible to exaggerate worries about a looming demographic crisis. Yet David Brindle's newspaper report (on the Commission for Social Care Inspection's forecast for the future of social care) does seem to suggest that a crisis is already happening, and that it will probably get a lot worse. Keep the extract from the newspaper article in front of you and jot down a short answer to each of the following questions:

(a) Is the crisis in care services being caused primarily by the 'growing longevity of disabled people' and the 'swelling elderly population', as mentioned in the article?

(b) What other causes of the 'care crisis' might there be?

(c) Why does there seem to be less of a public outcry about cutbacks and rationing of social care services, compared to rationing health care?

Comment

(a) Rising numbers of older and disabled people needing care are certainly one cause of the problem of finding enough carers and resources to cope, just as rising (or falling) numbers of children cause headaches for those who are trying to plan future numbers of school places. These are the problems of coping with changes in *demand* for services.

(b) However, there's also the question of *supply* (of money, facilities, paid carers and informal carers) to cope with demand. Arguably, the perennial problems of social care are due as much – if not more – to its Cinderella status and to shortfalls in government spending on care services as they are to steadily rising demand. But note that although David Brindle does highlight the significance of the shrinking role of the state, many newspaper reports like this still put a lot of emphasis on rising numbers of older and disabled people as 'the problem'.

(c) There could be a number of reasons for this, including the continuing popularity of the NHS and the importance attached to free health services by the majority of the population. However, as Brindle (2007) suggests, another key reason is that 'many people are unaware of what is happening' in social care and 'have unrealistic expectations' of what services are available. This is borne out by the carer Lynda Wisbach's comment (in the quotation from Butler, 2007, above) that 'nobody notices the crisis in social care till it happens to them'. Brindle points to evidence that as many as 'a third of adults thought they would automatically get free home care in their old age and only 10% thought they would have to pay for it entirely from their own pocket' (Brindle, 2007, p. 1).

Direct Payments may be thought of as a more economic and cost-effective way of providing social care and increasing choice. However, the Audit Commission (2006) reported that although people want more choice, they do not want to pay more taxes to get more choice. In ten councils surveyed for its study of the costs and benefits of increasing choice, Direct Payments were costing more than they saved. Although money was saved by service users arranging and administering their own care, extra costs were incurred in supporting users and training staff. The study suggests that the way to make savings is to ensure that the value of

Direct Payments is less than the sums paid to service providers. The implication of this is that the provision of social care may increasingly fall back on family and friends who can be employed more cheaply as personal assistants.

5.2 Drawing comparisons

When we're reflecting on the challenges facing social care in the UK, it's important to recognise that they are not unique and that other European countries have been grappling with similar problems. Sweden, for instance, had to make significant changes to its care policy following a severe economic crisis in the 1990s. Swedish social care, for example, 'has become more and more targeted towards the oldest age group, but also this group experienced a decrease in the provision of services' (Palme et al., 2002, p. 340). And according to Sundstrom and Tortosa (1999, p. 343), the changes in Sweden were achieved by 'sharpening … needs assessments and [raising] fees to discourage users with lesser needs'.

The rationalisation of social care in Sweden took place in a country that has a worldwide reputation for its welfare state and top-notch public services for all. Arguably, therefore, if cutbacks to social care can happen in Sweden they can happen anywhere. However, it's important to keep this example in perspective. Social care services might have been reduced in Sweden, but they are still very comprehensive and extensive. As Revill (2007) explains, the most an older person, for instance, would pay towards their care was about £90 a month (in 2006–07). Swedish social care is funded mainly from general taxation and is provided by local councils or municipalities: 'unlike in England, the pensioners' personal savings or property assets are not taken into account when assessing their ability to pay' (Revill, 2007, p. 17). Bearing this in mind, have a look at the following example and then complete the next activity:

> Inga Mollerborn sits in her fourth-floor flat on the outskirts of Stockholm … Her lifeline is now her carer, Annelie Brunstorp, who does her best to cheer her up and make her feel there is still meaning to her life.
>
> Confused and upset, what Inga needs most is company … [and] … it is a practical and smiling Annelie who comes into her flat each morning, makes her a bowl of strawberries and cream, with a milky coffee, and sits down to discuss what shopping she will need that day. The amount of support that Inga receives in her own home – some 25 hours a week altogether and up to seven visits a day from Annelie – is hugely generous compared with the package that would be on offer in England.
>
> In Sweden, a high level of funding enables the elderly to stay at home rather than go into care – and they pay only a small contribution towards the cost of it …
>
> For many families in England, this kind of personalised care … will never be attainable. Only those who are deemed to have very complex medical needs, such as being completely bedridden, would ever receive so many hours of care at home.
>
> (Revill, 2007, p. 16)

Inga Mollerborn, aged 91, receives up to seven visits a day from her carer Annelie Brunstorp

Activity 14 Social care in Sweden

Allow about 10 minutes

Reread the extract from the article on Inga Mollerborn and the personal care she is receiving in Stockholm. As you do this, compare the service Inga receives with what you know about social care in the UK. Then carry out the following exercises:

(a) Jot down two points about the quality and amount of Inga Mollerborn's personal care that you thought were outstanding compared with what's available in the UK.

(b) Imagine that you've gone to Stockholm to find out more about their social care services. Still with the example of Inga Mollerborn's care in mind, write down two questions that you'd like to ask a Swedish expert about social care in Sweden generally.

Comment

(a) We thought that several things about Inga Mollerborn's care service were outstanding – and, compared with what's available in every part of the UK, almost too good to be true! The number of hours of care per week that are provided are clearly outstanding, especially when you consider that Inga is getting these hours even though she is not seriously ill or physically disabled. (Inga appears to have some difficulties with walking, to judge from the photo, but no chronic illnesses are reported – although she is said to need 'cheering up' and to be 'confused and upset', suggesting that she might be experiencing loneliness and depression.) Another aspect of her care that struck us was the continuity – there is potential for a strong bond to develop between Inga and her carer, Annelie, and Inga doesn't have to contend with frequent changes of care workers. All in all, Inga seems to be receiving very personalised, high-quality care.

(b) Inga's example is a very telling one, but we have to remember that it was cited in a journalistic report on social care in Sweden. This means that the report gives a very striking individual example, but it leaves us wondering how representative of the whole Swedish care system Inga's example is. This isn't to say that it need be *un*representative, but we don't know from this brief report whether all Swedish care is as generous and of such high quality for all groups (e.g. younger disabled people). So the two questions we would like to ask the Swedish expert are:

- We've heard about cutbacks to social care services in Sweden. Do they mean that only very old people living alone like Inga can get this amount of care, and that people in their late seventies, for instance, or younger disabled people living together, might not get anything like the care Inga gets?
- Is the care service Inga receives in Stockholm typical of the whole of Sweden? Or do the amounts and quality of personal care vary a lot from one local authority to another, depending on their priorities?

The different approach to social care in Sweden shows us that, while every country has its problems, there is a range of options and choices to be made over care policy and how well funded care services will be. We can now see this happening *within* the UK. As mentioned earlier, devolution is introducing more and more divergence in health and social care between the 'national' policies of Scotland, Northern Ireland, Wales and England.

Right across Europe, let alone within the UK, governments face a common set of pressures on care policy – for instance, economic pressures and how to raise enough tax to pay for care services, the rising cost of care and the steadily rising demand for services in an ageing population.

If these pressures were being dealt with in the same way by every government, every country's policies on health and social care would be going in the same direction. But this doesn't seem to be happening (Motel-Klingebiel et al., 2005). Distinctive national policies remain – if anything, they are getting *more* different from, rather than more similar to, each other. Thus, the amounts of resources devoted to care services still seem to be shaped very much by the welfare traditions and cultures of each country or nation.

Key points

- In the twenty-first century, some sixty years after the founding of the welfare state, social care remains the poor relation next to the NHS.
- The 'crisis' in social care in the UK is often put down to *rising demand,* but it can be argued that this crisis is due more to *inadequate supply* (under-resourcing).
- Increasing choice and control through self-directed care arrangements, such as Direct Payments, is not a cheap option. In order to make savings, there is a risk of care provision falling back on family and friends.
- There are striking differences between the UK and other countries, such as Sweden, in the priority given to social care and the amount invested in it. These differences show that social care does not always have to be the 'Cinderella' of the welfare state.

Conclusion

In this unit we have looked at various aspects of the context of care. We hope that, in doing this, you have also been able to reflect on many of the issues and questions that have been raised earlier in the course. Our main concern was to help you to think about health and social care 'in the round' and to see care as a whole, rather than as a series of different topics chopped into different units. In drawing the threads together, we looked at what kind of society the UK has become in the twenty-first century and at what kinds of challenges, problems and opportunities this society has thrown up for the world of care.

Perhaps the single most important conclusion to draw from all this is that the UK's increasingly diverse and fragmented society will require a very different kind of welfare state from the traditional system that was set up in the last century. It has become clear that the health and social care services of the future will increasingly have to take into account the growing diversity of the UK's population – in terms of ethnic make-up, family or household structures and care norms, patterns of health and illness, gaps in living standards and 'consumer' expectations. The traditional welfare state concept of equality – 'one size fits all' – has become increasingly out of date. As the example of racial and ethnic diversity showed, treating everyone in the same way is likely to result in *greater* inequality and failure to match care services appropriately to the people who need them. Health and social care services will therefore have to become more varied, diverse and flexible if they are to stay in tune with the changing context of a postmodern society.

Learning skills: Getting yourself into good shape for the exam

You have thought quite a lot about the process of revising for the exam, but it's also a good idea to think in advance about how to 'tune yourself up' just before the exam, as you may find that you can't think about this calmly when the time arrives. It's mainly a matter of thinking carefully about what you are hoping to get out of yourself. Let's assume that you aren't going to be struck by supernatural inspiration in the exam room, and that you'll just have to rely on what an ordinary mind and body can achieve in three hours. How can you give yourself the best chance of a peak performance? Activity 15 may help you to answer that question.

Reader

Activity 15 Tuning up for the exam

Allow about 25 minutes

You can get some ideas about how to manage your final preparation for the exam from Section 12.5 of *The Good Study Guide* (pages 356–60). Read this now.

Comment

Here are some general principles you can draw out from your reading:

- Don't expect to be doing deep, creative *thinking* in an exam.
- Spend a high proportion of the time *writing* directly *on the topics* of the questions.

- *Reveal* as much as possible of *your knowledge and understanding* of the course.

All of these point to having your knowledge well organised in advance. In other words, you need to:

- get your knowledge of the course 'boiled down' to condensed, well-structured notes, so that it's quickly accessible at a moment's notice
- keep practising with exam-type questions until you have a slick technique for picking out key words and sketching out a plan
- be very clear about the three-part structure of the paper and which questions you have prepared yourself to answer
- prepare yourself to be disciplined in your use of time in the exam.

Perhaps you feel guilty about not having studied every part of the course in detail, and worry that you ought to strive for a miracle of detailed revision. Perhaps you feel that you ought to try to make yourself understand the course much better in order to write 'clever' answers. The truth is more ordinary. To do your best you simply need to be realistic, well organised, well practised and well planned. That is how to produce a peak performance. And these are things you still have time to achieve.

End-of-unit checklist

Now that you have completed this unit you should be able to:

- describe some major social trends that are likely to have a significant impact on health and social care today and in the future
- outline some key developments in health and social care policy since 2000
- identify ways in which control and choice are exercised in health and social care at the global, national and individual levels.

References

Alvarez-Rosete, A., Bevan, G., Mays, N. and Dixon, J. (2005) 'Effect of diverging policy across the NHS', *British Medical Journal*, vol. 331, pp. 946–50.

Alzheimer's Society (2004) *Drugs for the Treatment of Alzheimer's Disease* [online], www.alzheimers.org.uk/downloads/alzheimers_society_submission_to_nice_review_of_drugs_2004.pdf (Accessed 2 November 2008).

Arber, S. and Ginn, J. (2006) 'Ageing and gender: diversity and change', *Social Trends 34*, Norwich, The Stationery Office.

Audit Commission (2006) *Choosing Well: Analysing the Costs and Benefits of Choice in Local Public Services*, London, Audit Commission.

Barriaux, M. and Boseley, S. (2006) 'Third drug firm joins lawsuit against Nice', *Guardian*, 18 November [online], www.guardian.co.uk/medicine/story/0,,1951300,00.html (Accessed 2 November 2008).

Blakemore, K. (2000) 'Care and support – the example of ageing migrants' in Liu, W.T. and Kendig, H. (eds) *Who Should Care for the Elderly? An East–West Value Divide*, Singapore, Singapore University Press.

Blakemore, K. and Boneham, M. (1994) *Age, Race and Ethnicity: A Comparative Approach*, Buckingham, Open University Press.

Brindle, D. (2007) 'Families told elderly care crisis looming', *Guardian*, 10 January [online], www.guardian.co.uk/uk/2007/jan/10/topstories3.longtermcare (Accessed 29 November 2008).

Butler, P. (2007) 'Need for a new package deal?', *Guardian, Society*, 10 January [online], www.guardian.co.uk/society/2007/jan/10/socialcare.longtermcare (Accessed 29 November 2008).

Coates, D. (2005) *Prolonged Labour: The Slow Birth of New Labour Britain*, Basingstoke, Palgrave Macmillan.

Commission for Social Care Inspection (CSCI) (2004) *Direct Payments: What are the Barriers?*, London, Commission for Social Care Inspection.

Commission for Social Care Inspection (CSCI) (2008) *The State of Social Care in England 2006–07*, London, Commission for Social Care Inspection.

Dalley, G. (1998) 'Health and social welfare policy' in Bernard, M. and Phillips, J. (eds) *The Social Policy of Old Age*, London, Centre for Policy on Ageing.

Department of Health (DH) (2007) *Community Care Statistics 2006–07: Referrals, Assessments and Packages of Care for Adults, England*, The Information Centre [online], www.ic.nhs.uk (Accessed 29 November 2008).

Evans, R. and Boseley, S. (2006) 'Drug firms' lobby tactics revealed', *Guardian*, 28 September [online], www.guardian.co.uk/society/2006/sep/28/health.politics (Accessed 29 November 2008).

Health Education Authority (2000) *Black and Ethnic Minority Groups in England: The Second Health and Lifestyles Survey*, London, Health Education Authority.

Health Survey for England (2000) *The Health of Older People*, National Statistics, London, The Stationery Office.

Hennessy, P. (2007) *Having It So Good: Britain in the Fifties*, Harmondsworth, Penguin.

Henwood, M. (2008) 'Here to stay', *Community Care*, 20 March, p. 30.

Henwood, M. and Hudson, B. (2007) 'The road ahead', *Community Care*, 15 November, pp. 32–3.

Marmot, M. (2004) *Status Syndrome: How Your Social Standing Directly Affects Your Health and Life Expectancy*, London, Bloomsbury.

Maynard, A. (2006) Radio interview, *World at One*, BBC Radio 4, 17 November.

McKenzie, K., Bhui, K., Nanchahal, K. and Blizard, B. (2008) 'Suicide rates in people of South Asian origin in England and Wales: 1993–2003', *British Journal of Psychiatry*, vol. 193, no. 5, pp. 406–9.

Modood, T., Berthoud, R., Lakey, J., Nazroo, J., Smith, P., Virdee, S. and Beishon, S. (1997) *Ethnic Minorities in Britain: Diversity and Disadvantage*, London, Policy Studies Institute.

Motel-Klingebiel, A., Tesch-Roemer, C. and von Kondratowitz, H. (2005) 'Welfare states do not crowd out the family: evidence for mixed responsibility from comparative analyses', *Ageing and Society*, vol. 25, no. 6, pp. 863–82.

Mullan, P. (2000) *The Imaginary Time Bomb: Why an Ageing Population is not a Social Problem*, London, Tauris.

Nazroo, J. (2001) *Ethnicity, Class and Health*, London, Policy Studies Institute.

Netten, A. (2005) 'Personal social services' in Powell, M., Bauld, L. and Clarke, K. (eds) *Social Policy Review 17: Analysis and Debates in Social Policy, 2005*, Bristol, The Policy Press.

Office for National Statistics (ONS) (2004) *Social Trends 34*, Norwich, The Stationery Office.

Office for National Statistics (ONS) (2008) *Expenditure on Health Care in the UK* [online], www.statistics.gov.uk/articles/nojournal/ExpenditureonHealth08.pdf (Accessed 29 November 2008).

Palme, J., Bergmark, A., Backman, O., Estrada, F., Fritzell, J., Lundberg, O., Sjoberg, O. and Szebehely, M. (2002) 'Welfare trends in Sweden: balancing the books for the 1990s', *Journal of European Social Policy*, vol. 12, no. 4, pp. 329–46.

Pierson, J. (2002) *Tackling Social Exclusion*, London, Routledge.

Powell, M. (ed.) (1999) *New Labour, New Welfare State?*, Bristol, The Policy Press.

Revill, J. (2007) 'No one is left without care if they are poor', *Observer*, 24 June, pp. 16–17.

Shaw, M. and Davey Smith, G. (2005) 'Health inequalities and New Labour: how the promises compare with real progress', *British Medical Journal*, vol. 330, pp. 1016–21.

Sundstrom, G. and Tortosa, M.A. (1999) 'The effects of rationing home-help services in Spain and Sweden: a comparative analysis', *Ageing and Society*, vol. 19, pp. 343–61.

Taylor, S. and Field, D. (eds) (2007) *Sociology of Health and Health Care* (4th edn), Oxford, Blackwell.

Toynbee, P. (2006a) 'If Cameron can climb on my caravan, anything is possible', *Guardian*, 23 November [online], www.guardian.co.uk/commentisfree/2006/nov/23/comment.conservatives (Accessed 29 November 2008).

Toynbee, P. (2006b) 'This sinister assault reeks of political opportunism', *Guardian*, 24 October [online], www.guardian.co.uk/Columnists/Column/0,,1929840,00.html (Accessed 2 November 2008).

Toynbee, P. and Walker, D. (2005) *Better or Worse? Has Labour Delivered?*, London, Bloomsbury.

Wilkinson, R. (1996) *Unhealthy Societies: The Afflictions of Inequality*, London, Routledge.

Unit 23

Course revision and review

Prepared for the course team by Andrew Northedge with contributions from Anne Fletcher and Fiona Barnes

Contents

Introduction

When you reached the end of Unit 22 you completed the learning programme for K101. Perhaps you wondered at times whether you would make it to the end – but you did! Congratulations!

Now in this final unit you pull the course together and prepare for the exam, to give yourself the best possible chance of achieving the result you deserve. Section 1 gives you a step-by-step guide through the process of *revising* the *content* of the course, as well as advice on getting your mind well exercised and limbered up. Then Section 2 looks at how you can *prepare* for the *exam* itself and includes guidance on how to use the Exam Notes Sheet that you take into the exam with you. You will probably find it helpful, as you work through Section 1, to start straight into some revising and get into the swing of it. But after a day or two, move on to Section 2 because you will gain more by reading it while you still have time to mull things over before the exam.

Section 3 provides you with some self-reflective activities to help you review what you have learned from K101, as well as a brief look ahead to what lies beyond the course. You may prefer to leave these until the exam is over. On the other hand, reflecting on how much your skills and knowledge have developed since you started K101 might give you a helpful pre-exam morale boost.

You may not have been looking forward to the weeks just ahead. However, revision can be an unexpectedly constructive and satisfying process. You will be surprised how much of the course comes back to you quickly, once you get launched into organised revising. And as you look back over the course, you will find lots of things starting to fit together. Connections and themes will begin to emerge, and ideas that seemed difficult before will start to make a lot more sense – at which point you will become aware just how much more you know now than when you started K101.

For many students, even the exam itself turns out to be a more positive experience than they imagined:

> The exam was NOTHING like I thought – you really do not have to remember the whole course and you'll be amazed what you remember!
>
> (Past student)

> I hadn't taken an exam for 40 years ... and it wasn't as difficult as I thought. I really dreaded it ... but now my certificate is framed and hanging on the wall, I am so proud. I am now doing a level 2 course. Keep going everyone, it really is worth it.
>
> (Past student)

Having come this far, you may as well 'go for it', as they say, and aim to get as much from the experience as you can.

1 Revising for the exam

Since starting K101 you are bound to have learned a tremendous amount from all the reading, DVD activities and assignment work, as well as from dialogue with tutors and other students. But a lot of that learning is probably buried now under other learning and much of it will be jumbled up in your mind. So a key aim of the next week or two is to bring what you have learned back into view and to organise it, to make it ready for use again. The most obvious motive for doing this is to get yourself into the best possible shape for taking the exam. Yet revising is a very valuable process in its own right. Having invested so much time in learning, you might as well have your new knowledge well organised and accessible, so that you can make use of it in future.

In Section 1.2 you are guided through the process of systematic revision, but first it is important to get yourself properly focused.

1.1 Getting ready to revise

You have already done valuable preparation for the exam in earlier units. Here is a summary of where in the course you did that.

Unit	Topic	What you did
12	Nature of K101 exam	You looked at the exam section of the Assessment Guide
16	Exploding exam myths	You read Sections 12.1 and 12.2 of *The Good Study Guide*
	Planning revision	You did a first sketch of a revision timetable and of which blocks you might revise, and sent this off with TMA 06
17	Memory	On the DVD you did an activity about memory
20	Nature of the exam paper	You explored the Specimen Exam Papers and Guide
	What exam answers are like	On the DVD, you marked two exam answers
	Common mistakes	You read Section 12.3 of *The Good Study Guide*
	Planning revision	You read Section 12.4 of *The Good Study Guide* – and sent off a fuller revision plan with TMA 07
21	Managing anxiety	On the DVD you did a quiz on anxiety
22	Tuning up for the exam	You read Section 12.5 of *The Good Study Guide*

If you weren't able to cover some of these properly at the time, or you want to remind yourself about them, go back and look at them again. Before you do so, though, complete the quiz in Activity 1 to check how much you know about the exam.

DVD

Activity 1 Exam facts quiz

Allow about 15 minutes

Check that you have a good working knowledge of the K101 exam. Find Block 6, Unit 23, Activity 1 on the DVD.

Comment

The K101 exam paper is quite simple and straightforward. However, it is important to have the basics of how it works fixed clearly in your mind. If you got some answers wrong and are not sure why, revisit Unit 20 and read the comment following Activity 7, or ask questions in the online forums.

As well as being clear about the nature of the K101 exam, it is important to think about the nature of the process of revising. In Unit 20, you read about this in Section 12.4 of *The Good Study Guide*. It is worth reminding yourself of what you read there.

Reader

Activity 2 Basic principles of revision

Allow about 15 minutes

Skim back through Section 12.4 of *The Good Study Guide*, as far as Section 12.4.6 (pages 346–50) to remind yourself of some of the basic principles of revising.

Comment

You have already begun to think about some of the principles set out in Sections 12.4.1 to 12.4.6 of *The Good Study Guide*. In this section of Unit 23 we look at some of these principles more closely.

As we noted above, one key principle is to get yourself well organised.

Setting up a filing system

For some of the activities in this unit we provide worksheets on the course website. First, you need a folder to save them to.

Activity 3 Downloading worksheets to a revision folder

Allow about 20 minutes

Double click on My Documents on your desktop and find your K101 folder. Then create a new folder inside that labelled 'Revision'. (If you can't remember how to do this, see Section 5 of Getting Started Online.)

Then go to 'More Resources' on the course website and click on the 'Revision Resources' tab. Find 'K101 Revision Grid Block 1', right click on it and click on Save As. Save it to the revision folder you have just created. (For help, see the instructions for downloading templates in Section 7.1 of Getting Started Online.)

Then save the revision grids for the other five blocks to your revision folder. Also save both of the K101 Revision Timetable documents to your revision folder.

Comment

You now have a folder for all your revision work and you have put copies of revision worksheets into it. You may also want to move earlier revision-related documents there.

While we are talking about folders, you will also find it useful to have spare cardboard folders, plus labels, to help you reorganise your K101 papers.

Deciding which blocks to revise

Before going further, you need to firm up your thinking on which blocks to revise. To help you decide, look at the block titles on the back cover of the blocks. Basically, Block 1 introduces three broad *categories of care* – care within families, health care and social care. Block 2 looks at how care affects our *lives* and our sense of who we are and who we belong with. Block 3 then shifts the focus to *communities* as a context of need and also as a source of support and care. Block 4 examines the influence of *environments* on care and support, and Block 5 explores how unacceptable care practice arises and how *safe care practice* is promoted. Finally, Block 6 reviews changes in *care policy* in the UK over the past sixty years.

For *Part I* of the exam paper you can select either Block 1 or Block 2 as your 'major'. However, you might also want to do some work on the 'minor'. For example, you might decide that you will answer on Block 1 unless the Block 2 question happens to be on Lennox Castle, in which case you will choose that because you enjoyed Goffman's ideas and learned a lot about the history of care institutions. If this were your strategy, you would revise Units 1, 2 and 3 thoroughly in order to be able to answer Question 1 on the paper, whichever unit it may focus on. But you would also revise Unit 7, in case Question 2 is on care institutions. In other words, it isn't necessarily a matter of choosing some blocks and ignoring others altogether. However, for both Part I and Part II, you need to be sure that for at least one block you have revised all three of the main units.

For *Part II* the choice is between Blocks 3, 4 and 5, so you might decide to 'major' on one, but perhaps do some work on another as a back-up and leave out the third.

Finally, for *Part III* you have a choice between Unit 21 and Unit 22. Whichever of these you choose, you need to revise it thoroughly so that you can answer on any part of it, although again you might also do some revising of the other unit to give yourself more flexibility.

To summarise, the minimum revision strategy, to ensure that there will be questions on the exam paper for which you have revised, is as follows.

Exam paper	You revise	Selected from	Number of units to revise
Part I	One entire block	Block 1 or Block 2	3 units
Part II	One entire block	Block 3 or Block 4 or Block 5	3 units
Part III	One unit	Unit 21 or Unit 22	1 unit
		Total	7 units

However, you may want to make time for revising additional material, to give yourself more room for manoeuvre in the exam.

Making a revision timetable

With the course completed, you can now focus fully on preparing for the exam, but you need to plan your time. You have already done some time planning for TMAs 06 and 07, which provides a helpful starting point, but now it's worth going into greater detail. It's very easy to spend too long revising one part of the course and then find that you haven't left time for other parts, or for doing other important activities that are part of preparing for an exam. And the first step in planning your time is to work out how much of it you have.

Activity 4 How much time do you have?

Allow about 25 minutes

- Remind yourself of the date of the K101 exam. Then find your new revision folder and open the K101 Revision Timetable. Down at the bottom of the timetable, type EXAM on the appropriate day of the final week. Next, type the exam date in the 'Date' column and, working back up the timetable, fill in dates all the way up the column. This should bring you to somewhere near the current date.
- Highlight the final two days before the exam. ('Select' the two days by clicking in the morning of the first and 'dragging' to the evening of the second. Then go to Format and Borders and Shading. Click on the Shading tab and select a pale colour [not yellow].) On those two days, you'll need to be thinking and working in a different way, so leave them out of your plans for now.
- Mark in any events you know about, such as a Revision Day School or a phone link-up.

From this point, you can either continue working on screen, or print the timetable and work by hand (or do both).

- Block out all the spaces in the timetable when you know you *won't* be able to study between now and the exam (e.g. fill spaces with 'XXXX'). Put a question mark against times you're unsure about.
- Think in terms of 'sessions' of roughly two hours and count up the number of sessions you have available for revision. Some of your sessions might be an hour or three hours long: just make a rough estimate. Don't worry about accuracy. Just get a general sense of the number of revision sessions you think you will have and make a note of this.

Comment

Although an exercise like this is very rough and ready, it is extremely useful. To give you something to compare with, we will consider the example of an imaginary student, Ashley. Let's say that Ashley has worked out that he should have time for twenty sessions of about two hours over a four-week period. In other words, he hopes to find about forty hours:

20 sessions of 2 hours = 40 hours.

With this amount of time he will be able to make a big difference to his performance in the exam. Is your available time similar to this? Don't worry if it isn't. You can use a shorter amount of time very effectively if you are highly focused and well organised. Also, you can make excellent use of 20 minutes here and half an hour there, rather than working in two-hour sessions.

You now have a rough estimate of the number of sessions available for your exam preparations. The next thing is to plan how to use them.

Activity 5 Thinking strategically about how to use your time

Allow about 10 minutes

The plan below shows four different kinds of revision activity, each of which is important. (They are discussed further on in this unit.) The plan also shows estimates of time allocated to each activity by our imaginary student, Ashley. Think about whether you would allocate your own revision time in a similar way.

Time allocation strategy

Revision activity	Allocation of time
Getting organised	5%
Revising K101 units	60%
Practising answers	25%
Revising with others	10%
Total	100%

On the second page of your K101 Revision Timetable you will see a similar table under the heading 'Time allocation strategy'. Put in figures of your own, checking that they add up to 100. You may decide to change these figures later as you discover which activities are most useful to you.

Converting Ashley's time allocation strategy into twenty sessions gives the following.

Session allocation

Revision activity	Allocation of sessions
Getting organised	1
Revising K101 units	12
Practising answers	5
Revising with others	2
Total	20

Find the session allocation table on your K101 Revision Timetable and in the space against 'Total' write the total number of revision sessions that you expect to have. Then put in a number against each revision activity, making sure they add up to the right total. Do your best to make the numbers of sessions reflect the percentages in the table above, but don't worry about precise calculations. This is just an exercise in shaping up a general strategy.

Comment

Ashley has allocated twelve sessions to revising blocks. If he is planning to revise seven units, then with twelve sessions he will be able to spend one and a half sessions on each and leave a little leeway for changes of plan, or for adding another unit he is particularly interested in. He also has eight sessions available for other revision activities. This looks like a workable strategy.

The purpose of this activity was to help you think in general terms about ways of using your revision time. Life can be 'messy', so you are unlikely to be able to stick precisely to your plans. Nevertheless, planning is vital if you are going to stay in control of the revision process. Otherwise, you may find yourself part way through revising a unit, worrying about whether you are using your time well – unsure whether to switch to another activity or just to plough on. Worrying and switching tasks can use up a lot of time unproductively, as well as undermining your confidence, whereas knowing that you are working at part of a larger plan enables you to focus confidently on what you are doing.

Activity 6 Planning the time you have

Allow about 25 minutes

Again we begin with Ashley.

(a) In your revision folder find the 'K101 Revision Timetable example' and open it. This is Ashley's revision timetable filled in for the first week. The units are labelled A, B and C, but obviously you would put in the unit numbers of the blocks you have chosen to revise.

(b) Take a few minutes to look through the example. Note that Ashley has put in the exam date and marked off the last two days. How many sessions has he fitted into the first week? Does the plan seem to make sense? Will Ashley be able to get through enough revision before the exam?

(c) Now go to your own K101 Revision Timetable and start to fill in your plans for the week ahead of you. Don't worry about getting it 'correct'. You'll be able to change your mind as many times as you like. As you fill in some possibilities you will probably become aware of others and start moving sessions around. Make adjustments until you feel you have a sensible plan. Then look at the strategy you drew up for Activity 5 and consider whether further adjustments are needed.

(If you have come to this exercise quite late, the current date may already be into the second, or even the third, week of the timetable, so start filling in from there. If, on the other hand, you have chosen to come to the exercise early, you might need to add a week on to the start of the timetable [Go to Table, Insert, Rows above].)

Comment

(a) Ashley's life may not be much like yours, but you can see the general idea of weaving a revision plan around the commitments of a busy life.

(b) Ashley has put in a Day School that his Regional Centre informed him about. (That will use up his two sessions of revising with others, so perhaps he needs to adjust his strategy to give more time to revising with others and less to something else.) Overall, he has fitted seven sessions into the first week of his revision timetable and by the end will have revised a block, as well as completing Unit 23. Also, Ashley has mixed in different types of sessions, such as going back over the units he's done, and practising sketching answers, so that he won't get too bogged down. The plan seems well thought out and, if he can stick to it, appears to allow plenty of time to complete revision of seven units before the exam, as well as having time for other revision activities.

(c) Don't spend ages refining your plan. Just make a first shot at it, save it and print it. This will get you started. You are bound to have to modify the plan as real life takes its toll, but that isn't a problem. Treat it as a 'working document'. It simply represents your latest thinking about how to use your time.

(If you are beginning your planning two or three weeks into the timetable provided, just make sure that you use whatever time you have to good advantage. You can achieve a remarkable amount in a short time if you are well focused.)

Now you have a strategy and a plan of action, so you are ready to start revising. You have just used up an hour or more (half a session) of your available time on this planning. However, it is time extremely well invested. You are now in a position to make the best use of the rest of your time.

1.2 Revising the K101 blocks

You can revise for exams in a variety of ways. But don't just plough ahead without a strategy, or you will get very bored, lost and downhearted. The key thing is to make it an active process that involves searching for, thinking about and working with K101 ideas and case studies. Nothing will happen if you simply try to reread the course, hoping it will just 'go in'.

Reader

Activity 7 Revising strategically

Allow about 10 minutes

Sections 12.4.7 to 12.4.9 (pages 350–3) of *The Good Study Guide* suggest some things not to do, and outline an approach you could try. Read them again to remind yourself.

Comment

In this section we take you step by step through a version of the revision technique you have just read about – the 'boiling down' approach – the general principles of which are illustrated in the diagram on page 352 of *The Good Study Guide*.

Using the revision grids

The next activity introduces you to the K101 revision grids by going carefully through one of them. We have selected the Block 3 revision grid, but you can apply the same principles to other blocks.

Activity 8 Getting to know the K101 revision grids

Allow about 25 minutes

(a) Find your revision folder and open the Block 3 revision grid. You will see that the left-hand side is packed with information, while the right-hand side is blank.

(b) Explore the left-hand side of the revision grid. The first column shows the titles of the three main teaching units in Block 3. The second column shows the section headings of the units. The third column is a list of the main case studies in each unit section and the main readings you were sent to. Look down the list to see whether there are things you recognise. The fourth column provides a selection of the ideas the unit was intended to introduce you to. Skim through and see whether they ring any bells.

(c) Why the blank space? What else is there for you to do? Has the grid not done the revision of Block 3 for you? Think about whether, with this revision grid alongside you, you could sit down now and write an answer to a Block 3 exam question. If not, what would you need to do first in order to be able to write a decent exam answer?

Comment

(a) We have saved you a lot of time by compiling basic information about Block 3 at the left-hand side of the revision grid. The idea is that you use the left-hand side as a 'route map' to guide you on your second trip through Block 3 and that you write in the 'My notes' space at the right-hand side as you go. You can do this on screen, or you can print the revision grid to have alongside you as you revisit the course materials, filling it in by hand as you go. The first two columns of the revision grid are perfectly straightforward and the third you could have filled in yourself with a quick skim through the units. However, although the information is quite basic, it's very helpful to have it gathered together in one place and set out in a systematic way. It provides a handy reminder of the wide range of things you covered in Block 3 and how they sit alongside each other. The fourth column is what you would get if you skimmed through the key points at the end of each section and picked out key items quite selectively. So what you see in the revision grid is all taken from Block 3 but organised into a compact structure, instead of being scattered across the pages of units, readings and the DVD. This allows you to size it all up and 'get your head round it'.

(b) The unit titles in the first column provide the first structuring principle for a review of Block 3 – its broad division into the topics of 'neighbourhood', 'community' and 'diversity'. Then, in the second column, the section headings provide a second tier of structuring to aid your overall grasp of what the block covers. As you know from writing your essays, the way to explain ideas is to use case studies to illustrate what you want to say and to name authors and discuss their views. So Column 3 here provides a checklist of the main cases you might want to use in a Block 3 answer or the readings you might want to refer to. The list is not comprehensive, but that is the point of a table like this. It is selective, so that you can focus on the essentials. (Note that full titles of readings are not given here. You need to go back to the sources for those.) Finally, Column 4 is a companion to Column 3. It lists many of the main terms, concepts and ideas that you might be able to use in answering a question, which you would then illustrate using the cases in Column 3. Again, the list is not comprehensive. You can't hope to remember every detail of a block, so the revision grid helps you to pick out what is most important. (If you wish to, you can add other ideas in the 'My notes' column.)

(c) It would be very surprising if you could write a good exam answer with only the revision grid to go on. The information is much too brief. Take, for example, the first line in the grid for Unit 10 – you would be hard pressed to write more than a sentence or two about 'meanings of community' with only the words 'locality', 'social networks' and 'identity' to guide you. What you need in order to write a good answer are lots of ideas in your head, not a few words on a page. The words in the revision grid are of value only as reminders.

In order to make the revision grid useful to you, you have to go back to the units, the readings, the DVD and your essays and bring those ideas back to life again in your head. You need to remind yourself what the ideas in Column 4 are about, why they are important and how the case studies illustrate them. You did the hard work of making sense of the ideas when you read the units for the first time and wrote your essay. Now you just need to reactivate them, so that they are sitting in your head 'live' and ready for use. The revision grid makes this reactivation process more manageable by providing:

- reminders of what to look out for as you rummage through the course materials
- pegs on which to hang ideas after you have shaken out the creases.

Then, in the 'My notes' column you need to write reminders of how the ideas and the cases link together. Say you are revising Unit 10, for example. As you recall how the concept of 'social networks' is relevant to the residents of Thornhill, you might jot down 'Soc Net – Shelley, childcare', to remind yourself that there is a network diagram for Shelley and a discussion of her social network and childcare back-up. This wouldn't necessarily mean much to anyone else, but it will be meaningful to you.

What you write under 'My notes' converts the revision grid into a living document. Instead of just an organising tool, it becomes a representation of the ideas and information that you have reassembled in your mind. At the same time it becomes a personalised triggering system to help you bring ideas back to mind when you need them.

If you were revising Unit 10, you might end up with a 'My notes' box for Section 1 looking something like this.

Locality: e.g. Thornhill estate. Com. of Identity: David–Christian, Travellers.

Soc Ntwks (e.g. TPY) → practical, emotional, financial support: Shelley–childcare, Pauline–stroke–Elaine–reciprocity, Alexis(?). SN → better health (Putnam: life expectancy). Care services → help dev. SNs for vulnerable – e.g. Age concern proj. phone, fishing, bank (McLeod).

More likely, your notes would look quite different, because they would say whatever is helpful to *you*. But the example here gives an idea of the kind of thing to aim for. You don't want to copy out everything in the unit. You want just a few pithy notes that make sense to *you*.

At the same time as you are making these notes in the blank space, you might also want to highlight items in the columns to the left and perhaps write in extra notes of your own. You can also expand the boxes. It's up to you how you use a revision grid, but be wary of adding so much that it all becomes unmanageable. If you end up feeling you have let it get too complicated and messy, you can always download a fresh copy from the course website. (Give it a different name – e.g. *K101 Revision Grid Block 3b* – so that you don't lose the work you have done on the first version.)

Getting started on a block

To begin your revision of a block, first gather all the block materials together. Quickly reread the block introduction to remind yourself what the block sets out to do. Then start work on the first unit, but don't try to read it all through again. That would take too long and would be too boring. Use the block revision grid to help you look for things. You might want to replay some passages of the video and audio material (while keeping an eye on your time plan). Or you could skim through the transcripts and highlight a few points. You might go back to a Reader article and read just the introduction, then dip in at a few other points to remind yourself what it was about. Look back at any notes you made as you were working on the block. If your essay was related to the unit, read back through that too.

As you find items from the revision grid in the unit, use a different coloured highlighter to pick them out. Remind yourself what they are about. Make fresh notes in the unit margin if you feel like it, or write note sheets summarising unit sections or draw a mind map to summarise a unit – like the one in Figure 1. As you work on different resources, try to keep linking things back to the revision grid, but don't let the revision grid cramp your style. Do whatever helps you to engage *actively* with the unit (keeping an eye, of course, on your time plan). Work back and forth between the course materials and the grid. Use the grid as a working document that both shapes your revision and at the same time encapsulates the thoughts that revision brings back to your mind.

What you will end up with is a condensed guide to what is in the unit and a whole lot of freshly activated ideas in your head, which you can access quickly by looking at the notes you have made. By reviewing your revision grid a few times in the final days before the exam, you will be able to ensure that all those ideas are 'live' and ready for use in answering questions. The revision grid will be the tool you use for maintaining your mind in a state of readiness, but it is what is in your mind that will enable you to answer the questions.

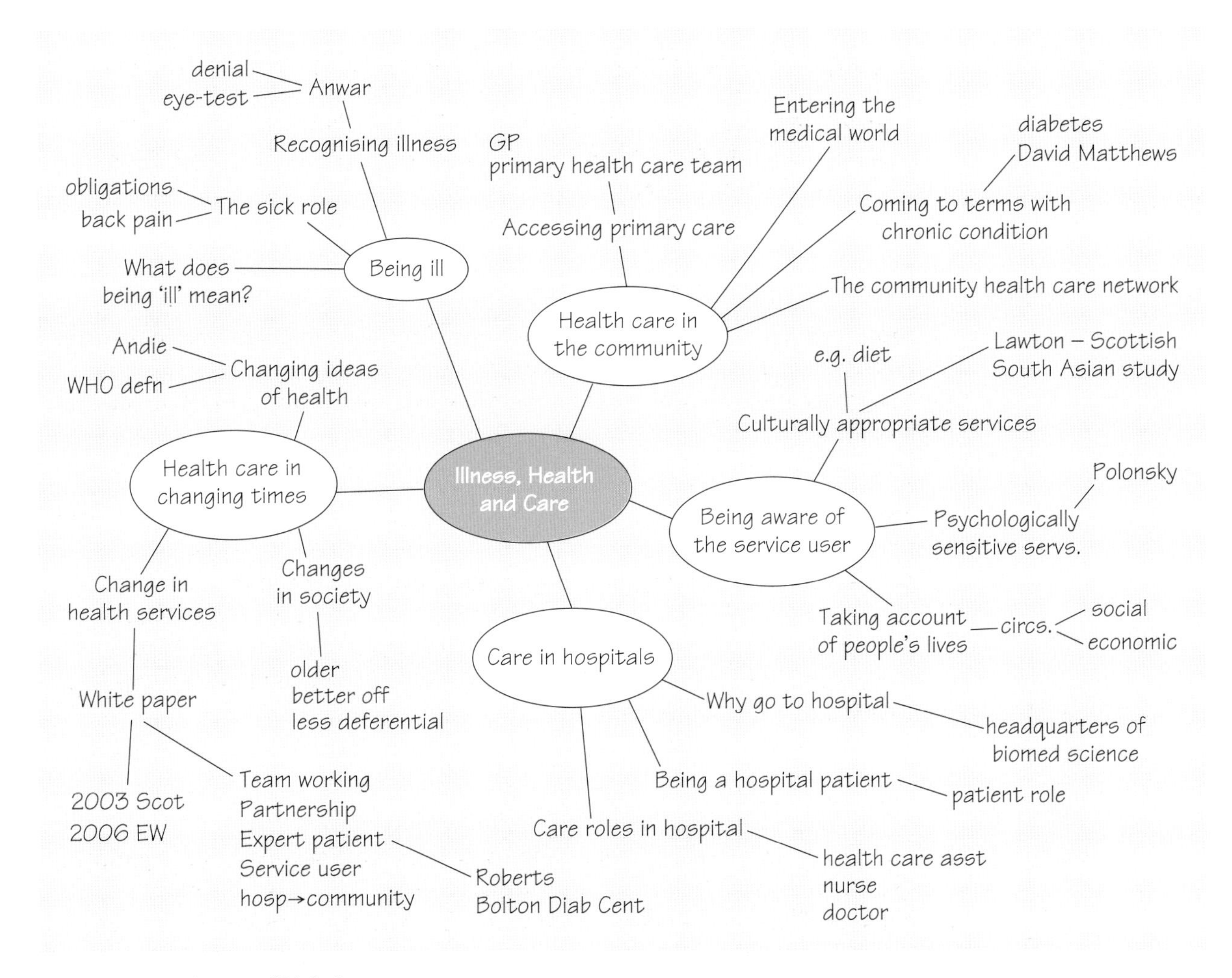

Figure 1 Mind map of Unit 2

Because a completed revision grid doesn't 'contain' knowledge, but is a referencing tool for accessing the knowledge of the person who completed it, it is a very personal document, of little value to anyone else. There is no point, for example, in borrowing a completed revision grid from somebody else. It will do nothing for your exam preparations because you don't have the knowledge in your head to correspond with the words in the grid. It's the process of writing notes in the grid as you revise that sets you up to write well in the exam. Looking at someone else's completed grid will trigger nothing, so it will only make you feel inadequate and anxious. However short of time you are, it is important to develop your own.

As this section has shown, revising is a process not of 'memorising' but of returning to information and ideas that once made sense to you, bringing them back to active life and summarising and organising them, so that they are ready for use. You have seen how to do this by systematically revisiting and engaging with previously studied material.

1.3 Other things to do

Systematic revision is the essential first step in making past course knowledge accessible to you, but there are other key activities that will prepare you for putting ideas and information to use quickly and effectively in an exam.

Practising answering questions

Tackling an exam question is not like the measured approach you take to a TMA question. You have to think quickly 'on your feet' – adapting what you know from your revision for the particular question you have been asked. So you need to give yourself plenty of practice at looking at a question and quickly working out a way to answer it. For this you need a supply of questions.

Getting hold of questions

The Specimen Exam Papers provide a start, but you need more. Past exam papers can be ordered from the Open University Students Association (OUSA) website, but you can also make up questions of your own, which in itself is an excellent way of revising, because it makes you reflect on what the course is about. Look again at Sections 12.4.11 and 12.4.13 of *The Good Study Guide* (pages 354 and 355) to remind yourself why.

In K101, the core questions at the start of each main unit provide a starting point for thinking up questions. For example, in Unit 6 'Group lives', the core questions are:

- What are groups and why are they important in health and social care?
- How do groups work?
- What are the strengths and weaknesses of self help groups in meeting care needs?
- Do face-to-face and virtual groups differ from one another?

Looking at these, you could imagine having an exam question along the lines of '*What are the advantages and disadvantages of groups in health and social care?*'

When you have tried making up a few questions, you could share them with other students in the online forums. The more you think about and discuss exam questions, the more insight you develop into ways of answering them.

Sketching answers

Once you have a supply of questions, give yourself plenty of practice at answering them. This doesn't have to involve a lot of writing. The most important part is working out what you are going to say. Read back through Section 12.4.12 of *The Good Study Guide* (pages 354–5) to remind yourself how this works.

Allow yourself 10 minutes (or just 5 minutes) to see how far you can get with sketching an answer outline without books or revision grids. Then go back to the relevant revision grid to flesh out your sketch. Finally, think about whether you have really answered the question and whether you have made enough use of K101 case material. You should be able to find ways of doing this exercise within the online forums, so that you can compare outlines with other students.

At first, you may find that you leave big gaps and go off track. But, with practice, you can become very efficient at breaking questions down and linking them back to ideas and cases from K101. The sketches don't need to be elaborate. You need only enough ideas to keep yourself writing for 45 to 50 minutes. You don't want to make your answer complicated, or you will hold up your writing. You need just a few trigger words to set you off in the right direction as you launch into the writing and to remind yourself of key points to cover.

Full answers

Some students decide to write out a full answer to a question to see how much they can write in an hour. This may be useful if you haven't taken an exam for a long time. But be aware of the cautions spelled out in Section 12.4.14 of *The Good Study Guide* (page 355). Don't be discouraged if your answer doesn't look nearly as good as your TMAs – it won't be and nobody expects it to be. You don't have time to write a carefully constructed, polished answer in an exam and you don't have to give quotations or details of references. The exam answers you marked for the DVD exercise in Unit 20 will have given you an idea of what to aim for, but remember that these were done with all the extra energy and urgency of real exam conditions.

Practice at handwriting

One reason for trying out a timed answer is to practise your handwriting. In fact, if you normally use a word processor it can be useful to do some regular handwriting practice as you come up to the exam, to build up the muscles in your hand and wrist. You could also have a supply of pens of different barrel sizes and switch between them from time to time, to reduce the strain on your hand.

Working with other people

One of the best ways to prepare for an exam is to keep talking with other students and to work together. By doing this, you will pick up revision tips and new ways of thinking about the course material, you will grow more confident about your revision and exam strategies and best of all, as noted in Section 12.4.15 of *The Good Study Guide* (pages 355–6), you will be able to keep things in proportion. If you can get to a Revision Day School or workshop, it will be time very well invested. The online forums will also offer plenty of scope for dialogue and collaborative working.

1.4 Managing stress

If you find yourself getting very stressed as you revise, seek advice. Talk to other students in the forums or by phone; phone your tutor; see your doctor. Don't just worry on your own. Try any relaxation techniques you have used in the past, perhaps for a driving test or for antenatal classes – for example, deep breathing. Look for other sources of advice, such as Sections 12.5.3 and 12.5.4 of *The Good Study Guide* (pages 358–9), or explore the 'Coping with exam stress' section of the Skills for OU Study pages of the Open University website, or search the internet for 'exam stress' and explore what is available.

To summarise, in this section you have looked at how to manage the process of revision – of going back over the course to reactivate your knowledge ready for rapid use in response to exam questions. In the next section you move on to think about how to manage the exam itself.

Key points

- Make sure you understand how the K101 exam works (see Activity 1).
- Get your course materials organised.
- Follow the guidance on choosing blocks and units to revise, so that you are sure of finding exam questions you have revised for.
- Make a revision timetable and keep updating it to take account of reality.
- Use the K101 revision grids to guide and organise your revision and to create triggers to your reawakened knowledge.
- Get plenty of practice at sketching outline answers to questions.
- Take advantage of collaborative working with other students.
- Take action if you start to feel stress building up.

2 Preparing for the exam

How can you ensure that you perform to the best of your abilities in the exam? As far as K101 is concerned, one thing you can do is prepare a sheet of notes to take into the exam.

2.1 Notes to take into the exam

As you know, you are allowed to take a single sheet of notes into the exam. But having invested time in completing the block revision grids, why have we not suggested taking those into the exam with you?

What kind of notes do you need in an exam?

By the time you enter the K101 exam your revision grids will have done their job. To have them in the exam would be a hindrance because they are too detailed. You need to think quickly and clearly as you write exam answers. Exams are about what you *know*, rather than what you can look up. In this, they are more like everyday life than like writing an essay. Normally, when someone asks you a question you 'think on your feet'. You don't go to a book and look up what to say – you say what you think. You rely on the knowledge in your head and answer to the best of your ability. That is what you do in an exam too.

Because you need to be able to think fast in an exam, it would work against you to be surrounded by notes. Time is too short for reading. You don't want your mind in 'taking-in' mode, you want it functioning smoothly in 'expressing' mode. In an exam you are too keyed up to read detailed information. Imagine having a lot of notes around you. You are suddenly struck by the thought that you ought to look something up, but you are so flustered that you take a couple of minutes to find it and, when you do, you can't focus well enough to make proper sense. Meanwhile, time is ticking away and you have lost your train of thought for your answer to the question. In contrast to this scenario, if you rely simply on what is in your head, you are likely to be much less anxious and more productive. An exam is a time to let your ideas flow, without worrying about whether you manage to include every possible angle or get every detail right. It is much more important to stay focused on the question. Extensive notes would simply distract you. All you require are a few memory joggers to get you started on the right track and to remind you of different angles you might cover. This is where the K101 Exam Notes Sheet comes in.

Preparing your Exam Notes Sheet

Find your Exam Notes Sheet. You have two copies, to allow you to make a draft and then a neat copy to take into the exam. Look at the general layout and read what is said on it. You will see that for each K101 unit there is a box for notes. You will also see that the boxes are modest in size. This will give you a pretty good idea of how few notes you need for an exam.

What might you write in the boxes on your Exam Notes Sheet? If you have worked up your revision grids and practised sketching outlines for answers to exam questions, you will have begun to see that, for each K101 unit, certain ideas, terms, names or readings stand out as key items that can be used in answer to a wide range of questions. For example, most answers to questions about

Unit 7 are likely to feature Lennox Castle, Goffman and total institutions. What you need in the exam notes boxes are trigger words like these. You don't need detailed information: detail will come back to you as you write. All you need are key words and phrases to show you where to start and, as your answer develops, to remind you what comes next. Figure 2 gives an example of the kind of notes you might draw up for Unit 5.

Block 2 notes

Unit 5	Unit 6
Life stories - identity Jordan - Susan McGladdery Ryan & Walker Bowlby - attachment - scripts Illness & identity - Mick & Owen Late life remembering Butler, Kitwood - Kate Attachment - trauma	

Block 3 notes

Unit 9	Unit 10

Figure 2 Exam notes on Unit 5

If you haven't revised Unit 5, the notes in Figure 2 won't look much. But if you have done a revision grid for Unit 5, these words will trigger a great deal. There is a whole story to tell about each of Jordan, Mick, Owen and Kate. There is a lot to say about the work of Ryan and Walker, Bowlby, Butler and Kitwood. And there is plenty to explain about ideas such as identity and attachment. These few words (just twenty-six) are enough to give you the basis for answering a Unit 5 question, provided you have revised Unit 5 and have all that material in your head. Of course, you would probably want to select a few different words and perhaps set them out differently, to reflect your particular take on the unit. But this is about the scale of what will be useful. Much more, and you will start to get muddled in your answers and make yourself anxious.

The idea is that you complete one of these boxes for each unit you have revised. Consequently, if you have opted to revise just seven units, there will be a fair amount of blank space. That is good. You don't want lots of clutter to distract you.

Allow a reasonable amount of time for making these notes and don't leave it to the last few days, because you need to be thinking clearly. Making the notes will itself help you to consolidate and organise your knowledge. It's a good idea to sketch notes on a pad a few times first, before trying to fit them into the actual Exam Notes Sheet. If you make several drafts, you will probably be able to refine the notes down and get the ideas really clear in your mind in the process.

Proper use of the Exam Notes Sheet

K101 is unusual in having an Exam Notes Sheet. Because strict regulations apply to exams, it is important to set out clearly what is allowed. Here are the basic terms.

- You are allowed to take just one sheet of notes into the exam. You have been supplied with a printed sheet headed Exam Notes Sheet. Your notes must be written on this sheet. You will not be allowed to take any other note sheet into the exam.
- The idea is that you write a few words and phrases per unit, to serve as memory joggers. Twenty to fifty words per unit is a reasonable target. If you write a lot more than that you will begin to undermine your exam performance.
- You are expected to use the Exam Notes Sheet in the spirit intended. Don't cram information all over it in tiny writing. In particular, we are concerned that you don't try to include whole sentences or substantial quotations for use in an exam answer. That is not in the spirit of the Exam Notes Sheet, and in any case, as we explained above, it won't help you. You will write good answers by thinking clearly about the questions you have been asked, not by trying to stitch together pre-prepared material.
- Because we don't want you to be tempted to cram as much information as possible on to the Exam Notes Sheet – and because we don't want students who use the sheet in the intended way to feel that they might be disadvantaged in relation to others who don't – we have stipulated that writing sentences and paragraphs on the Exam Notes Sheet is not permitted.
- You will be required to hand in your Exam Notes Sheet with your answer booklet at the end of the exam. This will allow us to monitor that the sheets are being used in the manner intended.

2.2 Tactics in the exam

To get the best out of yourself you need to think very clearly about how you will organise yourself in the exam itself. It is important to do this some time in advance because you may be too busy or too keyed up later.

Reader DVD

Activity 9 A time plan for the exam

Allow about one hour

Read Section 12.5.2 of *The Good Study Guide* (pages 357–8).

Then find Block 6, Unit 23, Activity 9 on the DVD and make yourself an exam time plan. When you have made your plan:

- Read Section 12.6 of *The Good Study Guide* (pages 360–6). (You will have to make a few adjustments because *The Good Study Guide* talks about a paper that requires answers to four questions, whereas you will have to answer only three questions.)
- As you read, imagine yourself in the exam and think about how the ideas and suggestions apply to you.
- In particular, think about the diagram in Figure 12.3 on page 364. Does it make sense?
- Ask other students in the online forums what their exam tactics will be.

Comment

Having worked out your exam time plan, you know exactly how much time you have for thinking and writing in the exam, so you can be even more focused in your preparations. You have a clearer idea now of what you are trying to achieve. In your revision for the units of your chosen blocks you only need to assemble enough material to enable you to write for 50 minutes or thereabouts. As you build up an ever-clearer picture of the reality of the exam and what will help and what won't, you can target your efforts to make sure you get the very best out of yourself.

The more you are able to clarify your tactics and commit yourself to a plan of action, the less anxious you will feel when you are in the exam. Instead of worrying, you will be moving step by step through the stages of your plan.

2.3 One week to go

As you get to within about a week of the exam, you need to be sure that you have checked all the details of the exam arrangements and that you know exactly what to do.

Reader DVD

Activity 10 An exam preparation checklist

Allow about 30 minutes

Look quickly at Section 12.5.5 of *The Good Study Guide* (page 359), to remind yourself why this is important.

Find the Examination Arrangements Booklet you will have been sent. (If you can't find it, you can download a copy from the StudentHome website – click on the 'Study support' tab and then the 'Guide to assessment' button, and you will find a link to it on that page.) Skim through it and highlight any items that are relevant to you.

Then find Block 6, Unit 23, Activity 10 on the DVD to create a checklist for yourself.

Comment

If you are reading this a week before the exam, go ahead and work through the first part of your K101 Exam Preparation Checklist. Otherwise, keep it handy and use it at the appropriate time.

During the final week your activities will probably be shifting from wider ranging revision of the course to more focused work on reviewing your revision grids, refining your Exam Notes Sheet and practising sketching answer outlines. By this time, you will have made your choices about what to cover from the course and gathered together the knowledge you are going take into the exam. From this point, the emphasis is on refining your notes and limbering up your question-answering reflexes. Reread Sections 12.5.3 and 12.5.4 of *The Good Study Guide* (pages 358–9) to help you reflect on the way you are working and feeling in these last days of preparation.

The final two days

By the final day or two you will find yourself functioning noticeably differently, so don't leave any basic revision till then. Let yourself switch into an overviewing, consolidating and question-answering mode. Check over your Exam Notes Sheet. Check over your exam time plan. Put your books away and concentrate only on the grids. Don't disturb carefully laid plans at the last minute. To keep yourself in a realistic but positive frame of mind read Section 12.7 of *The Good Study Guide* (page 367). Plan something nice for after the exam, and take the evening before the exam off and try to get a good night's sleep.

The day itself

On the day itself all you have to do is get up, have breakfast, go through the exam day checklist and set off at the appropriate time. Don't bother to think about the exam. You have done everything you can and you have your Exam Notes Sheet with you, so give your mind a rest. For a few thoughts on how to respond to being in the exam itself, read Section 12.5.6 of *The Good Study Guide* (page 360).

If anything goes wrong – say you arrive late or are taken ill during the exam – speak to the invigilator, who will tell you what to do. If something prevents you from attending the exam at all (e.g. a sudden illness), contact your National or Regional Centre straight away. You can find details of how to report such events in the Examination Arrangements Booklet. Whatever happens, you will be able to rescue the situation – at worst by arranging to take the exam at a later date.

To finish up with, here are some tips about the exam day from experienced Open University students:

- If you revise thoroughly there is nothing to worry about on the day.
- Put together pens and other things you need for the exam beforehand.
- Prepare for the journey to the exam – double check your transport.
- Relax the night before.
- Arrive in plenty of time.

- Take deep breaths before the exam.
- Don't panic when you read the questions.
- Read the paper twice and take three deep breaths before answering anything.
- Read the questions through carefully – a few times if needed.
- Underline key words.
- Before beginning answers, 'brainstorming' is a good way of remembering most topics.
- Plan your answer – for example, draw a mind map.
- Remember that all the other students are in the same boat – and it's NOT the end of the world if you fail.

Finally, good luck from the course team!

3 A review of your learning

We end the course with a look back at all you have achieved and a brief look forward to what follows on.

3.1 What have you learned from K101?

After months of intensive learning, what have you gained from K101? There are two activities in this section. The first follows up the self-ratings of learning skills you did in Unit 12. The second invites you to review some of the K101 learning outcomes and consider how you would offer evidence of what you have achieved in relation to them.

DVD

Activity 11 How well have your learning skills progressed during K101?

Allow about 30 minutes

You have been asked to spend a lot of time during K101 reading about learning skills, reflecting on them and doing exercises. What has it all achieved? For a final review of your learning skills across the course, go to Block 6, Unit 23, Activity 11 on the DVD.

Comment

You should now be in a good position to weigh up how good a student you are, what your strengths are and where you can develop further. You should also be able to give a confident account of your learning skills to anyone who wants to know. And you should be able to approach any future studies with confidence and skill, knowing that you have the insight and resilience to overcome whatever challenges you face.

Having reviewed the development of your learning skills, now you can review what you have learned from the course itself.

DVD

Activity 12 Your achievements in terms of the K101 learning outcomes

Allow about 20 minutes

K101 is a wide ranging course with various learning strands and you have probably learned so many different kinds of things that it is hard to bring it all to mind. However, it can be valuable to review what you have learned so that you can take confidence in your many achievements, particularly when you are considering future courses. Moreover, other people, particularly employers, may want to know what you know. But they will want specific examples, not vague claims, so it can be useful to make some notes of these in readiness, while the course is still fresh in your mind. If you are interested in exploring this, go to Block 6, Unit 23, Activity 12 on the DVD.

Comment

Usually you don't need to describe your knowledge, you just know it. But sometimes you may be required to give an account of what you know. At some point in the future, when it is relevant, you may want to return to this activity.

Activities 11 and 12 have focused quite specifically on learning skills and on learning outcomes, but what about more general things that you have learned from K101? Has studying the course led you to think differently about care? Has it changed how you see yourself as a user of care services? If you work in care, has it changed how you see your work? Did working with the five K101 principles of care practice lead you to reflect on your values? Do you see discussions of care issues in the news and have a clearer grasp of what is at stake? You might want to reflect on some of these questions with other students in the online forums, before everyone goes off for a well-deserved break.

No doubt you will continue to reflect on what you learned from K101 in the months ahead, as you keep making connections with care-related issues in the world around you. But are you going to build on all that learning by taking further courses?

3.2 What will you learn in future?

Now that you have succeeded in reaching the end of K101, you may be feeling that you would like to carry on studying. If so, the skills you have learned in K101 will stand you in very good stead. Perhaps you have registered already for a course for next year, but if not now is a good time to think about it – while you are still in study mode and while you still have your student group 'around you'. Have you discussed your plans with each other? It can be very helpful.

Back in Unit 12, you explored the course information on the Open University website and wrote some first thoughts about possible future courses, which you sent off with TMA 04. Have things moved on since then? Perhaps you found time to visit the Course Choice forum for advice. (If not, you could look in there now. It may not be 'live' at the moment, but you can still read the messages.) Anyway, if you are still thinking things over, it might be useful to look back at your earlier ideas.

DVD

Activity 13 Revisiting your first thoughts about future courses

Allow about 20 minutes

If you are unsure about what to study next year, or even whether to study, why not review what you wrote four months ago? Revisit Block 3, Unit 12, Activity 5 on the DVD. Skim through the activity. Open the Activity Notes for Tasks 1 and 3 to see whether your thoughts have changed since then. If they have, make alterations and print the sheets so that you have a record. Perhaps it would also be useful to revisit some of the web pages to which Task 1 directs you.

Comment

Since you wrote your first thoughts halfway through the course, you have studied new areas and you also know a lot more about your capabilities as a student, so perhaps your perspective has changed. Maybe it is time to seek fresh advice.

If you are unsure about things, talk with your tutor. You could also contact the Open University enquiry service on +(0)845 300 6090, or your Open University National or Regional Centre. Or you could look for online advice at www.open.ac.uk/study.

You don't need to wait to get your K101 result before starting the process of registering for another course. Now is as good a time as any.

Whatever your choice, we hope very much that you have enjoyed K101 and learned some interesting things.

Very best wishes from the K101 course team!

Course team

Production team

Andrew Northedge (Chair)

Joanna Bornat (Deputy Chair)

Corinne De Souza (Course Manager)

Maureen Richards (Course Manager)

Sarah Shelley (Course Team Assistant)

Dorothy Atkinson

Fiona Barnes

Ken Blakemore

Hilary Brown

Joyce Cavaye

Anne Fletcher

Marion Hall

Julia Johnson

Rebecca Jones

Ann Martin

Mo McPhail

Ingrid Nix

Sheila Peace

Mary Twomey

Jan Walmsley

Naomi Watson

Fran Wiles

Media production team

Phil Greaney, Fiona Harris, Matthew Moran, Jenny Nockles (Editorial Media Developers); Paul Bishop, Ray Guo (Interactive Media Developers); Vicky Eves (Graphic Artist); Debbie Crouch (Designer); Judy Thomas (Librarian); Adrian Bickers, Michelle Woolley (Media Project Managers); Philippa Broadbent, Ann Carter, Kim Dulson, Siggy Martin (Print Buyers); Sas Amoah, Bisiola Arogundade (Media Assistants); Martin Chiverton (Executive Sound and Vision Producer); Carole Brown (Sound and Vision Assistant); Gail Block, Melisa Ekdoghan, Phil Gauron, Annie Morgan (Clear Focus Productions); Lindsay Brigham, Phil Coleman (Integrated Vocational Route); Richard Norris, Harry Venning (Cartoonists).

External assessor

Jon Glasby, University of Birmingham

Critical readers

John Adams, James Blewett, Ian Buchanan, Barry Cooper, Celia Davies, Monica Dowling, Sarah Earle, Ric Estee-Wale, Elizabeth Forbat, Sandy Fraser, Sally French, Teresa Geraghty, Leonie Kellaher, Aine MacNamara, Mick McCormick, Paul McDonald, Ann Mitchell, Alun Morgan, Janet Seden, Sam Parboteah, Vijay Patel, Jenny Pearce, Lucy Rai, Martin Robb, Angela Russell, Patricia Taylor, Linda Walker.

Developmental testers

John Dow, Tamsin Dunsdon, Trisha Shaw, Susan Underwood, Mark Vine.

Acknowledgements

Grateful acknowledgement is made to the following sources for permission to reproduce material in this book.

Cover

Copyright: © Juice images/punchstock

Text

Page 96: Brindle, D. 'Families told elderly care crises looming', *The Guardian*, 10 January.

Table/Illustration/Cartoon/Other

Page 11: © Reg speller/Getty Images and © PA/PA Archive/PA Photos; Page 15: © PA/PA Archive/PA Photos; Page16: © Mary Evans Picture Library and © Alamy; © Maggie Murray/photofusion; Page 17: © Whitelaw, G., *The Daily Herald*; Page 20: © Haywood Magee/Getty Images; Topical Press Agency/Getty Images and Central Press/Getty Images; Page 23: © Maggie Murray/photofusion; Mirrorpix; Page 26: © Alamy; Page 31: © Alamy; Page 37: Professor Peter Townsend; Page 38: © GMB Britains General Union; Page 63: © Sean Dempsey/PA Archive/PA; Page 66: © Stephen Kelly/PA Wire/PA Photos and © MLA East Midlands; Page 68: www.statistics.gov.uk; Page 70: © BBC News Interactive; Page 73: Copyright © Adrian Sherratt/Alamy; Page 77: © Bert Hardy/Getty Images and © Andrew Parsons/PA Archive/PA Photos.